Teacher

# Language
## Seatwork Text

# 2

## Grammar • Creative Writing • Reading Comprehension

This workbook is correlated with the *A Beka Book* language arts program, including *Letters and Sounds 2, Writing with Phonics 2,* and *Spelling and Poetry 2.* It is intended to be used as a seatwork book.

**by** Shela Conrad

**Editors**
Laurel Hicks
Naomi Sleeth
Gloria Rigsby

**Design** Jim Bailey

**Art** Jim Bailey,
John Halbach, Paul De Luna,
Stephanie Blatch, Nate Horton,
Tim Solomon, John Ball,
Omar Garcia, David Chan

A Beka Book®
A MINISTRY OF
PENSACOLA CHRISTIAN COLLEGE
PENSACOLA, FLORIDA 32523-9160

# Teaching *Language 2*

*Language 2* provides an interesting introduction to written language for the second-grade student, integrating grammar, creative writing, and reading comprehension skills in a delightful manner. It has been designed for use with the Second Grade Curriculum. No special time period needs to be set aside for language at this grade level. Many of the concepts are taught during class phonics time.

One page is provided for each day of the school year. Lesson numbers are located at the bottom of each page. Give a brief explanation of the work during Seatwork Explanation time, being sure to give help with the understanding of new rules. Students should then work the pages independently. A few creative writing stories could be started together in class and finished in Seatwork. Whenever time allows, check each child's work, and help students to correct their errors.

Second graders have many words in their speaking vocabulary that they may not have seen in printed form. The Word Challenge word lists (near the back of the book) have been compiled to provide an opportunity for students to read commonly used words. The lists may also be used for reference during creative writing activities.

At the beginning of the school year, remove the good work tickets and certificates from the back of each student's book. Cut them apart and file them. Distribute these tickets and certificates to individual students as they master the appropriate tasks.

## Objectives

Upon completion of the work in *Language 2*, students should have mastered the following skills:

1. Recognize and write a complete sentence, a question, and an exclamation.
2. Be able to capitalize the first word in a sentence, days of the week, months of the year, special holidays, word *I,* and names of people.
3. Put correct punctuation at end of a sentence (period, question mark, or exclamation point).
4. Be able to read and comprehend sentences and short stories.
5. Write interesting sentences and short stories.
6. Know and use suffixes and prefixes.
7. Recognize and work with compound words, rhyming words, opposite words, same-meaning words, singular and plural words, singular possessive words, and contractions.
8. Alphabetize words.
9. Use the following words correctly: *sit, sat, set; to, too, two; may, can; learn, teach; right, write; blue, blew.*

## Creative Writing

One of the primary goals of language study is to teach students to write clearly and concisely. *Language 2* builds creative writing skills in a carefully planned sequence so students can write their thoughts in an imaginative and grammatically correct manner.

## Reading Comprehension

To complete many of the activities in this work-text, students must comprehend the written words, sentences, and paragraphs. Reading comprehension comes easily to students who have a good background in phonics, and their reading comprehension skills will be sharpened by the comprehension activities provided throughout *Language 2*.

**Third Edition**

Copyright © 1996, 1986, 1978 Pensacola Christian College
All rights reserved. Printed in U.S.A. 1998

Hi! I'm Mr. Floppy Fish, your language helper.

**Complete** each sentence.   Answers vary.

1. My name is _____.

2. My teacher's name is _____.

3. I like to eat _____.

4. I am _____ years old.

*Language Skills:* Demonstrating comprehension by correctly completing sentences; spelling answers correctly; improving penmanship skills.

1

**Match** the word with its picture.

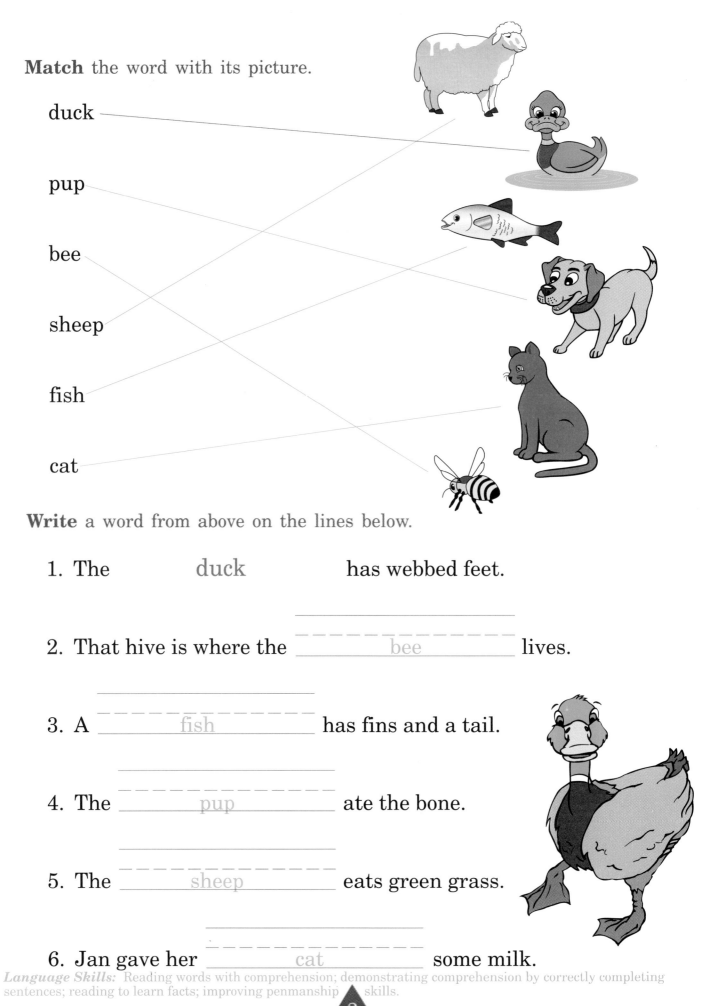

duck

pup

bee

sheep

fish

cat

**Write** a word from above on the lines below.

1. The        duck                has webbed feet.

2. That hive is where the _____ bee _____ lives.

3. A _____ fish _____ has fins and a tail.

4. The _____ pup _____ ate the bone.

5. The _____ sheep _____ eats green grass.

6. Jan gave her _____ cat _____ some milk.

*Language Skills:* Reading words with comprehension; demonstrating comprehension by correctly completing sentences; reading to learn facts; improving penmanship skills.

**Match** the word with its picture.

run

make

jump

wave

melt

**Write** a word from above on the lines below.

1. The ice cube will _____melt_____.

2. The frog can _____jump_____.

3. Mary will _____wave_____ goodbye.

4. Sue can _____make_____ pretty pictures.

5. Bob can _____run_____ fast.

*Language Skills:* Reading words with comprehension; demonstrating comprehension by correctly completing sentences; improving penmanship skills.

*Language 2* Lesson 3

**Match** the sentence with its picture.

1.  The cake tasted good.

2.  The pig lay in the mud.

3.  Kim will sleep well.

4.  Mother cooked the meat for dinner.

5.  The snake ate a bug.

6. Dave will cut the grass.

*Language Skills:* Demonstrating comprehension by matching pictures with sentence descriptions.

**Complete** each sentence by drawing a line to the correct ending.

1. I like to go                    fin.

2. The fish has a            fishing.

3. I use a fishing            lake.

4. My boat is                snack.

5. I fish in the              pole.

6. I will eat fish for a        red.

*Language Skills:* Demonstrating comprehension by choosing the correct word to complete a sentence.

*Language 2*    Lesson 5

**Finish** the sentences.   Answers vary.

1. The frog is _____ .

2. I like to eat _____ .

3. The hen laid an _____ .

4. He went _____ .

5. Dot saw a _____ in the pond.

6. _____ fell into the lake.

7. _____ went home to rest.

*Language Skills:* Demonstrating comprehension by correctly completing sentences; improving penmanship skills.

**Finish** each sentence with a word from the margin.

**lake**

**net**

**Indian**

**ten**

1. The _Indian_ had a mule to ride.

2. He rode to the _lake_ to get a fish.

3. He had a pole and a _net_ with him.

4. He got _ten_ bass to eat.

*Language Skills:* Demonstrating comprehension by choosing the correct word to complete a sentence; improving penmanship skills.

*Language 2* Lesson 7

**Finish** the sentences using all the words in the box.

1. The ostrich has  **two long legs** .

    **two**        **legs**        **long**

2. Sam hit the ball _____ to the base _____ .

    **base**        **to**        **the**

3. The pig ate _____ the big corncob _____ .

    **corncob**        **big**        **the**

4. Mom had one _____ big box to get _____ .

    **big**        **to**        **box**        **get**

5. God is with us _____ all the time _____ .

    **time**        **all**        **the**

6. The sun will _____ shine all day _____ .

    **all**        **shine**        **day**

*Language Skills:* Demonstrating comprehension by correctly arranging words to complete a sentence; improving penmanship skills.

Lesson 8    *Language 2*

8

**Finish** each sentence with a word from the margin.

**white**

**meal**

**sea**

**gulls**

**six**

1. Tim went deep _____ sea _____ fishing.

2. The boat was green and _____ white _____.

3. He got _____ six _____ fish on his pole.

4. Tim had a fine _____ meal _____ of fish for lunch.

5. The sea _____ gulls _____ rode on the boat, too.

*Language Skills:* Demonstrating comprehension by choosing the correct word to complete a sentence; improving penmanship skills.

9

**Finish** the sentences.  Answers vary.

1. The _____ was green.

2. The boy had a _____ and a ball.

3. Mom will bake a big _____ .

4. I have _____ toes.

5. The _____ was ringing.

6. Jan can jog up the _____ .

7. The cherry _____ was good.

8. Joe told a funny _____ .

*Language Skills:* Demonstrating comprehension by correctly completing sentences; improving penmanship skills.

When two words end with the same vowel and consonant sound, we say they **rhyme.**

| dish | hop |
|------|-----|
| fish | pop |

Concept introduced in Phonics/Language 2 Curriculum, lesson 10.

**Circle** the rhyming words.

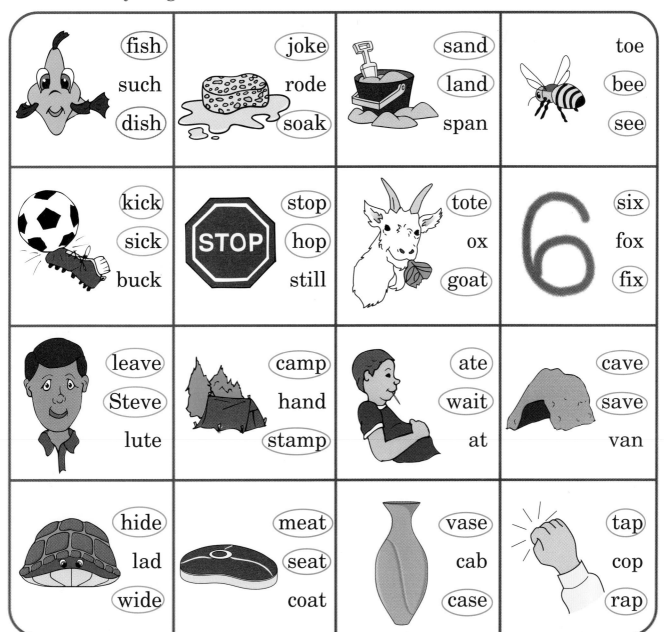

| fish | joke | sand | toe |
| such | rode | land | bee |
| dish | soak | span | see |

| kick | stop | tote | six |
| sick | hop | ox | fox |
| buck | still | goat | fix |

| leave | camp | ate | cave |
| Steve | hand | wait | save |
| lute | stamp | at | van |

| hide | meat | vase | tap |
| lad | seat | cab | cop |
| wide | coat | case | rap |

**Language Skills:** Analyzing words to identify rhyming words; reading words with comprehension.

*Language 2* Lesson 11

> ## A syllable is a part of a word.
> but / ter / fly

Concept introduced in Phonics/Language 2 Curriculum, lesson 11.

**Write** the number of syllables you hear in each word. Clapping will help you decide how many syllables are in each word.

1. spelling ___2___
2. rabbit ___2___
3. Saturday ___3___
4. sixteen ___2___
5. March ___1___
6. conduct ___2___
7. hurting ___2___

8. Tuesday ___2___
9. forty ___2___
10. clouded ___2___
11. October ___3___
12. parch ___1___
13. woodpecker ___3___
14. trusted ___2___

**Circle** the rhyming words in each box.

| | | | | | |
|---|---|---|---|---|---|
| (fix) | tax | (mix) | (dive) | fine | (five) |
| bone | (fin) | (win) | (hide) | (side) | six |
| (boat) | (coat) | bill | (deck) | dill | (neck) |
| (can) | land | (van) | will | (well) | (bell) |

*Language Skills:* Syllabicating and determining the number of syllables in a word; analyzing words to identify rhyming words.

**Finish** the sentences using the words in the box.

| bone | dive | boat | five |
|------|------|------|------|

1. Bill can _____dive_____ into the water.

2. I had _____five_____ fish in my box.

3. The dog had a _____bone_____.

4. We can sail in the _____boat_____.

**Remember!**

A syllable is a part of a word.

**Write** the number of syllables you hear in each word.

1. Sunday ___2___

2. rose ___1___

3. kitchen ___2___

4. robin ___2___

5. candy ___2___

6. bumblebee ___3___

7. May ___1___

8. puppy ___2___

**Language Skills:** Demonstrating comprehension by choosing the correct word to complete a sentence; improving penmanship skills.

*Language 2* Lesson 13

> A sentence begins with a capital letter.
> **H**e is funny.

Concept introduced in Phonics/Language 2 Curriculum, lesson 12.

**Write** the sentences correctly.

1. we went to the pond.

   We went to the pond.

2. i saw ten fish in the pond.

   I saw ten fish in the pond.

3. jan fed the ducks.

   Jan fed the ducks.

4. don set out the picnic lunch.

   Don set out the picnic lunch.

5. lee and Dee are twins.

   Lee and Dee are twins.

6. frogs make good pets.

   Frogs make good pets.

7. dee will take home a frog.

   Dee will take home a frog.

*Language Skills:* Beginning a sentence with a capital letter; reading sentences with comprehension; improving penmanship skills.

*Remember!*

A sentence begins with a capital letter.

**Finish** each sentence correctly.
**Copy** the sentence on the line below.  Answers vary.

1. the dog is brown .     The dog is brown.

2. the sun can _____ .

3. may I go to the _____ ?

4. the boy can kick _____ .

*Language Skills:* Beginning a sentence with a capital letter; demonstrating comprehension by correctly completing sentences; improving penmanship skills.

> A sentence usually ends with a period.
>
> Todd is having fun**.**

Concept introduced in Phonics/Language 2 Curriculum, lesson 14.

**Copy** each sentence; **add** the period.

1. Tim had ten boards    Tim had ten boards.

2. Tom had some rope and nails

   Tom had some rope and nails.

3. Tim and Tom made a hut to hide in

   Tim and Tom made a hut to hide in.

4. Beth can look and look

   Beth can look and look.

5. She will not find them

   She will not find them.

*Language Skills:* Ending a telling sentence with a period; reading sentences with comprehension; improving penmanship skills.

> david played his harp for the king
> (**incorrect**)
> _____
> **D**avid played his harp for the king.
> (**correct**)

**Write** these sentences correctly.
Remember to begin with a capital letter and end with a period.

1. david kept his father's sheep

David kept his father's sheep.

2. he sang praises to God

He sang praises to God.

3. he loved God very much

He loved God very much.

4. god chose David to be king

God chose David to be king.

*Language Skills:* Recognizing that a telling sentence begins with a capital letter and ends with a period; reading sentences with comprehension; improving penmanship skills.

**Write** rhyming words.  Answers vary.

**bat — hat**

1. dill — <u>hill</u>

2. mad — <u>glad</u>

3. sob — <u>rob</u>

4. run — <u>fun</u>

5. hog — <u>log</u>

6. big — <u>wig</u>

7. set — <u>get</u>

8. tag — <u>bag</u>

9. fin — <u>tin</u>

10. mop — <u>plop</u>

**Copy** the sentence; **add** a period.

1. Pat has a fat rat

<u>Pat has a fat rat.</u>

2. Jan ran to the van

<u>Jan ran to the van.</u>

3. Brett will get a net

<u>Brett will get a net.</u>

***Language Skills:*** Analyzing words to write rhyming words; ending a telling sentence with a period; reading words and sentences with comprehension;      improving penmanship skills.

**Write** the sentences correctly.
Remember to begin with a capital letter and end with a period.

1. luke has a toy jet

   Luke has a toy jet.

2. it can go very fast

   It can go very fast.

3. dan likes to play with Luke

   Dan likes to play with Luke.

4. the jet got stuck in a tree

   The jet got stuck in a tree.

5. dan had to lift Luke up

   Dan had to lift Luke up.

*Language Skills:* Beginning a sentence with a capital letter; reading sentences with comprehension; improving penmanship skills.

*Language 2*   Lesson 19

A sentence is a group of words that expresses a complete thought.

Saw the fish.
(This is only part of a thought.)

Jane saw the fish.
(This is a complete thought.)

Concept introduced in Phonics/Language 2 Curriculum, lesson 17.

**Circle** yes if the group of words expresses a complete thought.
**Circle** no if the group of words does not express a complete thought.

yes (no) 1. The fish.

(yes) no 2. I see a boat.

yes (no) 3. The man is.

(yes) no 4. You can do it.

(yes) no 5. Shoes help our feet.

(yes) no 6. Moses loved God.

yes (no) 7. Pond frogs and snakes.

(yes) no 8. I put a stamp on the letter.

yes (no) 9. Combs and brushes.

yes (no) 10. May be lost.

*Language Skills:* Recognizing that a sentence makes a complete thought; analyzing groups of words to decide if a sentence; reading with comprehension.

**Circle** each group of words that expresses a complete thought.

1. (A bear loves to eat fish.)
   A bear loves to.

2. (Bears are very big animals.)
   Bears very big animals.

3. Have short tails.
   (They have short tails.)

4. (Some bears are brown.)
   Are brown.

5. Baby bear cubs.
   (Baby bears are called cubs.)

**Complete** the sentences.   **Copy** them on the lines below.   Answers vary.

1. Jan can

2. Praying is talking to

3. I love

*Language Skills:* Analyzing groups of words to decide if a sentence; ending a telling sentence with a period; reading with comprehension; improving penmanship ▲ skills.

*Language 2*   Lesson 21

**Mark** yes if the sentence is correct.  **Mark** no if the sentence is incorrect. Remember that a correct sentence begins with a capital letter and ends with a period.

○ yes  ● no    1. I like to go to the beach

● yes  ○ no    2. God is love.

○ yes  ○ no    3. we want to go home at three o'clock.

○ yes  ○ no    4. An octopus lives in the sea

○ yes  ○ no    5. The pup was brown and white.

○ yes  ○ no    6. Moses was hidden in the bulrushes

○ yes  ○ no    7. trucks help us to move things

○ yes  ○ no    8. Please do not quit.

**Copy** each sentence.  Remember to end each sentence with a period.

1. Pete went home to eat

Pete went home to eat.

2. Tim went with him

Tim went with him.

3. Brad was sad

Brad was sad.

*Language Skills:* Recognizing that a telling sentence begins with a capital letter and ends with a period; analyzing sentences to decide if written correctly;          reading sentences with comprehension; improving penmanship skills.

Finish each sentence, using all the words in the box.

1. I will _____ pray every day.

**pray   day   every**

2. I can _____ read my Bible.

**Bible   read   my**

3. Van liked to _____ go to church.

**go   church   to**

4. He will _____ bring a friend.

**friend   a   bring**

Write a sentence about each picture. Remember to begin with a capital letter and end with a period. Answers vary.

1. _____

2. _____

3. _____

*Language Skills:* Demonstrating comprehension by arranging words correctly to complete a sentence; ending a telling sentence with a period; using creative ability to          write a sentence describing a picture; beginning a sentence with a capital letter.

23

A root word is the word we begin with.

looking   (not a root word)
look    (root word)
looked    (not a root word)

Concept is introduced in the Phonics/Language 2 Curriculum in lesson 22.

**Circle** the root word in each box.

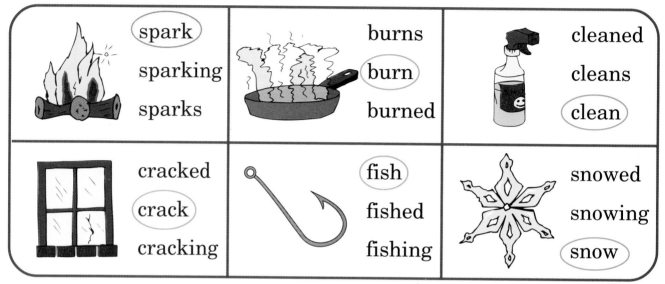

| | |
|---|---|
| (spark) sparking sparks | burns (burn) burned |
| cracked (crack) cracking | (fish) fished fishing |

cleaned cleans (clean)

snowed snowing (snow)

A suffix is a letter or a group of letters added to the end of a root word to make a new word.

plum — (root word)          frost — (root word)
plums — (root word + suffix)   frosting — (root word + suffix)

Concept is introduced in the Phonics/Language 2 Curriculum in lesson 22.

**Add** the suffix -s, -ing, or -ed to the root words.   Answers vary.

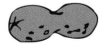   **crush — crushed**

1. stamp _____stamps_____          4. shell _____shelled_____

2. stump _____stumps_____          5. crash _____crashing_____

3. play _____playing_____          6. bless _____blessed_____

*Language Skills:* Analyzing words to identify the root word; forming words by adding the suffixes *s, ing,* or *ed* to root words (help students choose the correct suffix; the *s* cannot be added to crash or bless).

**blowing — blow**

**Write** the root words.

1. ducks     duck

2. jumping     jump

3. barked     bark

4. brushed     brush

5. sides     side

6. shooting     shoot

7. thinking     think

8. starts     start

9. prizes     prize

10. scuffing     scuff

**Write** a sentence for each picture.   Answers vary.

1.

2.

*Language Skills:* Analyzing words to identify the root word; reading words with comprehension; using creative ability to write a sentence describing a     picture; recognizing that a telling sentence begins with a capital letter and ends with a period.

25

**Add** the suffix -s, -ing, or -ed to the root words.   *Answers vary.*

1. hook       hooked

2. clock       clocks

3. worm       worms

4. hang       hangs

5. snow       snowing

6. frog       frogs

7. sea       seas

8. curl       curling

**Answer** the questions, using complete sentences.   *Answers vary.*

1. Do you like boats?     **Yes, I like boats.**

2. Can you go fishing on Saturday?

3. How many fish do you think you will get?

*Language Skills:* Forming words by adding the suffixes *s*, *ing*, or *ed* to root words (guide students as they form the words); answering questions with a sentence; recognizing that a telling sentence begins with a capital letter and ends with a period.

Lesson 26    *Language 2*

26

**Write** a sentence for each picture.  Answers vary.

1. _____

2. _____

3. _____

**Circle** yes if the group of words is a complete thought.
**Circle** no if it is not a complete thought.

| | | |
|---|---|---|
| (yes) | no | 1. A crab is a water animal. |
| yes | (no) | 2. Has eight legs and two claws. |
| (yes) | no | 3. Mr. Crab has a shell. |
| (yes) | no | 4. Some crabs can be eaten. |
| yes | (no) | 5. Is sometimes mean. |
| yes | (no) | 6. A white sand crab. |

*Language Skills:* Using creative ability to write a sentence describing a picture; recognizing that a telling
sentence begins with a capital letter and ends with a period; analyzing groups of words to decide if a sentence;
reading with comprehension.

*Language 2*    Lesson 27

A compound word is two words joined together to form one word.

sun + shine = sunshine

Concept is introduced in the Phonics/Language 2 Curriculum in lesson 26.

**Circle** each smaller word in these compound words.

1. (pan)(cake)

2. (street)(car)

3. (cup)(cake)

4. (milk)(man)

5. (rain)(coat)

6. (oat)(meal)

7. (dish)(pan)

8. (rain)(storm)

9. (pine)(apple)

10. (rail)(road)

11. (dust)(pan)

12. (shot)(gun)

13. (pork)(chop)

14. (in)(to)

15. (be)(side)

**Write** a sentence with each compound word.  Answers vary.

rainstorm  1. _____

cupcake 2. _____

into 3. _____

*Language Skills:* Identifying the root words in a compound word; using creative ability to write sentences including a compound word; recognizing that a sentence begins with a ★ capital letter and ends with the proper punctuation mark.

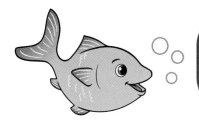

Things that are very different from each other are called **opposites.**

Concept is introduced in the Phonics/Language 2 Curriculum in lesson 27.

**Match** opposite words.

1. hot          awake        6. out         off

2. stop         open         7. on          work

3. asleep      thick         8. soft         father

4. thin          cold          9. play        loud

5. close        go           10. mother    in

**Write** yes if the group of words is a complete thought.
**Write** no if it is not.

   _yes_    1. I am the good shepherd.

   _yes_    2. The Lord is my rock.

   _no_    3. A bench is.

   _no_    4. One ship.

   _yes_    5. The car smashed into the truck.

   _yes_    6. The bird sings every day.

   _yes_    7. The girl can skate.

   _no_    8. The mouse's tail.

*Language Skills:* Identifying words with opposite meanings (antonyms); analyzing groups of words to decide if a sentence; reading with comprehension.

Color words tell us what things look like.

Match the color word with the picture.

white sand

black dog

red heart

yellow moon

blue ball

orange sun

brown cow

purple grapes

green grass

Finish the sentence. Answers vary.

My favorite color is _____

Language Skills: Identifying color words; demonstrating comprehension by matching a picture with the word description.

_____

_____

_____

**Finish** the sentences using color words.  Answers vary.

1. I like to eat   purple   grapes.

 

2. My hair is _____ brown _____ .

 

3. Our flag is _____ red _____ ,

_____ white _____ , and _____ blue _____ .

 

4. The sun and moon are _____ yellow _____ .

 

5. My bike is _____ orange _____ .

 

6. I saw a dog that was _____ black _____ .

 

7. I like apples that are _____ red _____ .

**purple**

**brown**

**yellow**

**orange**

**white**

**black**

**red**

**blue**

*Language Skills:* Demonstrating comprehension by choosing the best word or words to complete a sentence; improving penmanship skills.

31

ARGYLL HOME EDUCATION
SERVICES CENTRE      *Language 2*   Lesson 31

**Finish** the compound words.  Answers vary.

## in — side

1. her      self

5. rain      coat

2. sun      light

6. pine      apple

3. cup      cake

7. pan      cake

4. grand      father

8. basket      ball

**Add** the suffix -ed or -ing to these root words.
**Write** the word on the blank.  Answers vary.

## wink — winked

1. sing      singing

7. long      longing

2. jump      jumped

8. plant      planted

3. smack      smacking

9. whirl      whirling

4. list      listed

10. lick      licked

5. join      joining

11. catch      catching

6. camp      camped

12. lift      lifted

*Language Skills:* Forming compound words; forming words by adding the suffix *ed* or *ing* to root words; reading words with comprehension.

*Remember!*

A sentence is a group of words that expresses a complete thought. A sentence begins with a capital letter and usually ends with a period.

Here are two sentences together.
**Put** in the periods. **Circle** the letters that need a capital.
**Write** both sentences correctly on the lines.

1. (a) sea horse is a fish. (i)t has a tail.

   a. A sea horse is a fish.

   b. It has a tail.

2. (s)ea horses have one fin. (t)hey eat baby fish.

   a.           Sea horses have one fin.

   b.           They eat baby fish.

3. (s)ea horses are tiny. (t)hey have big eyes.

   a.           Sea horses are tiny.

   b.           They have big eyes.

*Language Skills:* Recognizing that a telling sentence begins with a capital letter and ends with a period; identifying sentences; improving penmanship skills.

There are seven days in a week.

| | |
|---|---|
| Sunday | Thursday |
| Monday | Friday |
| Tuesday | Saturday |
| Wednesday | |

Concept introduced in Phonics/Language 2 Curriculum, lesson 30.

**Finish** the sentences using the days of the week.

1. _____Sunday_____ is the day to go to church.

2. _____Monday_____ is the first school day.

3. We also go to school on _____Tuesday_____,

_____Wednesday_____, _____Thursday_____,

and _____Friday_____.

4. On _____Saturday_____ we play and have fun.

**Circle** one word in each row that tells about the picture.

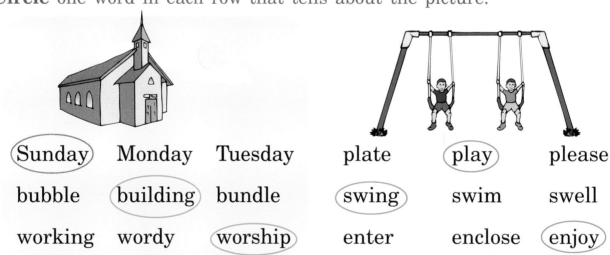

| | | | | | |
|---|---|---|---|---|---|
| (Sunday) | Monday | Tuesday | plate | (play) | please |
| bubble | (building) | bundle | (swing) | swim | swell |
| working | wordy | (worship) | enter | enclose | (enjoy) |

*Language Skills:* Learning the days of the week; demonstrating comprehension by choosing the correct day or days of the week to complete a sentence; improving penmanship skills; identifying words that describe a picture.

**Write** rhyming words.  *Answers vary.*

1. play     *day*       6. hush     *mush*

2. fry     *shy*       7. shell     *sell*

3. shot     *hot*       8. clip     *rip*

4. see     *bee*       9. brave     *cave*

5. clam     *slam*       10. smile     *mile*

**Write** sentences using these words.  You will need to add some words of your own to make these sentences complete.  *Answers vary.*

1. Monday     wash     clothes

2. Friday     shopping

3. Sunday     church

*Language Skills:* Analyzing words to form rhyming words; using creative ability to write sentences including given words; recognizing that a telling sentence begins with a capital letter and ends with a period.

> Words may be divided between double consonants.
>
> rib|bon

Concept introduced in Phonics/Language 2 Curriculum, lesson 34.

**Divide** between the double consonants.

1. b u t|t e r      5. h e l|l o      9. s o n|n e t

2. p e p|p e r      6. s u f|f e r    10. t u n|n e l

3. s k i p|p e r    7. b u t|t o n    11. k i t|t e n

4. w i n|n e r      8. h i d|d e n    12. p i l|l o w

**Word Challenge**    Can you match the words that mean almost the same? Optional

1. store         seat        6. tale        sick

2. lad           ship        7. ill         story

3. bench         boy         8. shut        evil

4. boat          sing        9. bad         small

5. chirp         shop        10. little     close

*Language Skills:* Syllabicating between double consonants (remind students that only the first consonant of a double consonant is sounded); identifying words that have similar meanings (synonyms).

**Finish** the sentences.

1. The snail has a    shell    for a house.

**shell — foot**

2. A snail moves very ____slowly____ .

**fast — slowly**

3. But a ____snail____ can get inside his shell very fast.

**snail — snake**

4. Snails eat green plants and ____leaves____ .

**leaves — life**

5. Some birds like to ____eat____ snails.

**play — eat**

6. Snails live on the land or in the ____water____ .

**grass — water**

*Language Skills:* Demonstrating comprehension by choosing the correct word to complete the sentence; reading to learn facts; improving penmanship skills.

**Finish** the sentences.

| eating | hatch | close |
| --- | --- | --- |

1. Most snails ___hatch___ from eggs.

2. Some snails ___close___ the door of their shell and hide.

3. People enjoy ___eating___ some snails.

**Add** -s, -ing, or -ed to the root words.
**Write** the new words. Answers vary.

**click — clicking**

1. water ___watering___          4. coat ___coats___

2. check ___checked___          5. point ___pointing___

3. bank ___banking___          6. walk ___walked___

*Language Skills:* Demonstrating comprehension by choosing the correct word to complete a sentence; reading to learn facts, forming words by adding the suffix s, *ing*, or *ed* to root words.

Draw a line to the picture that matches each sentence.

1. The rabbit is hopping in the grass.

2. Beth is raking leaves in the yard.

3. The fish are swimming in the brook.

4. Two boys are playing
   on the swings.

5. The clowns are jumping up and down.

*Language Skills:* Demonstrating comprehension by matching pictures with the sentence description.

© 1996 Pensacola Christian College • Not to be reproduced.     39     *Language 2*   Lesson 39

A word may be divided between a vowel and a consonant.

Bi|ble
chick|en

Concept introduced in Phonics/Language 2 Curriculum, lesson 37.

**Divide** these words between the vowel and the consonant.
**Divide** the ck words after the ck.

1. t a|b l e       5. p i|l o t       9. l a|b e l

2. f a|b l e       6. f l i c k|e r       10. o|p e n

3. s t a|b l e       7. s n i c k|e r       11. b e|g i n

4. c a|b l e       8. t i|g e r       12. a|c o r n

**Write** a sentence for each picture.   Answers vary.

1._____

2._____

3._____

*Language Skills:* Syllabicating between a vowel and a consonant; using creative ability to write a sentence describing a picture; recognizing that a telling sentence begins with a capital letter and ends with a period.

**Write** the day of the week that best completes the sentence.  Answers vary.

| | |
|---|---|
| **Sunday** | 1. On _____, I went to play ball at the park. |
| **Monday** | |
| **Tuesday** | 2. On _____, I visited my grandparents. |
| **Wednesday** | |
| **Thursday** | 3. I go to church on _____. |
| **Friday** | |
| **Saturday** | 4. _____ is my favorite day at school. |

**Place** a period where the sentence ends.
**Draw** a line through the words that are not needed.

1. Pat got six fish on Thursday. ~~in it~~

2. Brad is sick. ~~to her for~~

3. Tim went for a bike ride. ~~lost the~~

4. John rode home on the bus. ~~see on~~

5. Bev likes to bake. ~~out of on~~

6. Jim and I will run. ~~the loud~~

**Language Skills:** Demonstrating comprehension by choosing the correct day of the week to complete a sentence; analyzing a group of words to identify a sentence; ending a telling sentence with a period. (Help students do one or two of the sentences in the second exercise.)

*Language 2*   Lesson 41

> There are 12 months in a year.

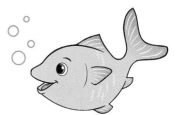

Concept introduced in Phonics/Language 2 Curriculum, lesson 40.

**Write** the correct month in each blank.

January

February

March

April

May

June

1. _____January_____ is a cold winter month.

2. In _____February_____ we have Washington's and Lincoln's birthdays.

3. The _____March_____ winds blow.

4. _____April_____ showers bring

    _____May_____ flowers.

5. _____June_____ is the beginning of summer.

**Circle** the sentence that tells about the picture.

1. (The turtle is eating his dinner.)
   The turtle is looking at the pond.

2. The snail hid in his shell.
   (The snail crept slowly along.)

*Language Skills:* Demonstrating comprehension by choosing the correct month that completes a sentence; choosing the sentence that describes a picture.

**Write** the correct month in each blank.

| | |
|---|---|
| **July** | 1. _____July_____ and _____August_____ are hot summer months. |
| **August** | |
| **September** | 2. In _____September_____, boys and girls go to school. |
| **October** | 3. The leaves fall in _____October_____. |
| **November** | 4. Thanksgiving Day is in _____November_____. |
| **December** | 5. Jesus' birthday is in _____December_____. |

**Circle** the words that rhyme with the first word in each box.

| look | right | chalk | clown |
|---|---|---|---|
| (took) | (flight) | perk | crow |
| (hook) | burst | (walk) | chosen |
| booth | knelt | nook | (frown) |
| goose | (might) | (talk) | (brown) |

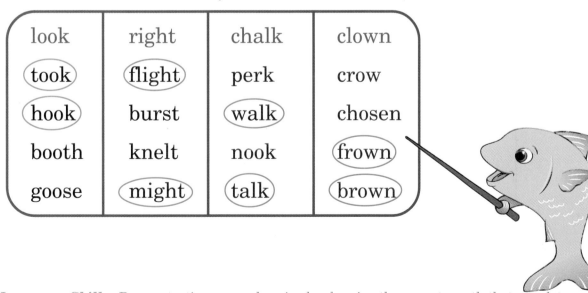

*Language Skills:* Demonstrating comprehension by choosing the correct month that completes a sentence; analyzing words to choose rhyming words.

43

> A word may be divided between two consonants that are not alike.
>
> tur|tle

Concept introduced in Phonics/Language 2 Curriculum, lesson 41.

**Divide** these words between two consonants that are not alike.
**Write** how many syllables are in each.

1. b u c k|l e  _2_

2. c h u c k|l e  _2_

3. s p a r k|l e  _2_

4. p i c k|l e  _2_

5. i n|s t r u c t  _2_

6. p o w|d e r  _2_

7. u n|d e r  _2_

8. y e s|t e r|d a y  _3_

**Mark** the ○ under the correct picture.

I live in the water.  I might sting you!

○                   ⬤                   ○

**Write** two sentences about a green tree frog that you found.  Answers vary.

_____

_____

_____

_____

_____

_____

**Language Skills:** Syllabicating between two unlike consonants. Demonstrating comprehension by solving a riddle; using creative ability to write sentences; recognizing that a telling sentence begins with a capital letter and ends with a period. (Encourage students to write interesting and varied sentences.)

Lesson 44   *Language 2*                    44

**Write** sentences using the following words.  You will need to add some words of your own to make the sentences complete.  Answers vary.

**yellow moon — The big yellow moon rose over the pond.**

1. red apple

2. brown acorn

3. orange leaf

4. green worm

*Language Skills:* Using creative ability to write sentences including two given words; recognizing that a telling sentence begins with a capital letter and ends with a period; improving penmanship skills.

45

**Write** a sentence with each group of words below.

1. seashells  found  the  Dee

   **Dee found the seashells.**

2. my  is  best  Steve  friend

   Steve is my best friend.

3. ate  Sally  lunch  for  shrimp

   Sally ate shrimp for lunch.

4. beach  went  Lee  to  the

   Lee went to the beach.

5. got  fish  Dale  big  a

   Dale got a big fish.

*Language Skills:* Demonstrating comprehension and organization by correctly arranging words to form a sentence; ending a telling sentence with a period; improving penmanship skills.

Lesson 46   *Language 2*                                46

When a one-syllable root word ends with a short vowel and a consonant, double the consonant before adding a suffix beginning with a vowel.

| | |
|---|---|
| rub (root word) | rubbed (suffix -*ed*) |
| rubs (suffix -*s*) | rubbing (suffix -*ing*) |

Concept introduced in Phonics/Language 2 Curriculum, lesson 45.

**Add** -s to the root word.  Write the word.

**skip — skips**

1. rip        rips        3. flap        flaps

2. nod        nods        4. plan        plans

**Add** -ed to the root word.  Write the word.

**skip — skipped**

1. rip        ripped        3. flap        flapped

2. nod        nodded        4. plan        planned

**Add** -ing to the root word.  Write the word.

**skip — skipping**

1. rip        ripping        3. flap        flapping

2. nod        nodding        4. plan        planning

*Language Skills:* Forming words by adding the suffixes *s, ed,* and *ing* to root words that end with a short vowel and a consonant; improving penmanship skills.

*Language 2*   Lesson 47

**Add** -ed or -ing to the root word.  Write the word.  *Answers vary.*

## hop — hopped

1. hum _____humming_____          5. flip _____flipped_____

2. mop _____mopped_____           6. spot _____spotted_____

3. grin _____grinning_____        7. dip _____dipping_____

4. shut _____shutting_____        8. dot _____dotted_____

**Write** three sentences about goldfish in a bowl.

## Three Goldfish

_____

_____

_____

_____

_____

_____

*Language Skills:* Forming words by adding the suffixes *ed* or *ing* to root words; using creative ability to write sentences; recognizing that a sentence begins with a capital letter and ends with the proper punctuation mark.

Here are two sentences together. **Put** in the periods. **Circle** the letters that need to be capitals. **Write** both sentences on the lines.

1. (y)ou are on time. (y)ou are not late.

   a. _You are on time._

   b. _You are not late._

2. (t)he boat was at the dock. (i)t was a tugboat.

   a. _The boat was at the dock._

   b. _It was a tugboat._

**Match** the opposites.

| | | | | | |
|---|---|---|---|---|---|
| 1. pull | **under** | | 5. dark | **frown** |
| 2. sister | **push** | | 6. smile | **stop** |
| 3. over | **take** | | 7. start | **walk** |
| 4. give | **brother** | | 8. run | **light** |

*Language Skills:* Recognizing that a telling sentence begins with a capital letter and ends with a period; identifying sentences; identifying antonyms.

An apostrophe and *s* show that something belongs to someone.

Bill's book
(means the book belongs to Bill)

Concept introduced in Phonics/Language 2 Curriculum, lesson 47.

**Add** 's to these words.

**Ann's**

1. Mary__'s__

2. Sue__'s__

3. Joe__'s__

4. Ed__'s__

5. Linda__'s__

6. Rick__'s__

**Rewrite** these phrases with 's.

**the dog of Susie — Susie's dog**

1. the bed of Dale

Dale's bed

2. the toy of Vick

Vick's toy

3. the bear of Ben

Ben's bear

4. the dress of Pam

Pam's dress

**Write** two sentences about what Don will do with his new sled the first time it snows.

**Don's Sled**

Answers vary.

**Language Skills:** Using an apostrophe and an *s* to indicate ownership; demonstrating comprehension by rewriting phrases with an apostrophe and an *s*; using creative ability to write sentences; recognizing that a sentence begins with a capital letter and ends with the proper punctuation mark.

**Add** 's to these words. **Write** the words.

1. Fred_'s_ foot

        Fred's foot

2. Steve_'s_ car

        Steve's car

3. Dee_'s_ doll

        Dee's doll

4. Jack_'s_ dog

        Jack's dog

**Finish** the sentences. **Write** the answer in the puzzle.

| snow | sled | penguins | ice |

1. ____Penguins____ are birds that do not fly.

2. Jon and Jan went down the hill on their ____sled____ .

3. Mother made some ____ice____ cream.

4. ____Snow____ is cold, white flakes of ice.

*Language Skills:* Using an apostrophe and an *s* to indicate ownership; demonstrating comprehension by choosing the correct word to complete a sentence; solving a crossword puzzle.

Some sentences ask a question. They begin with a capital letter and end with a question mark.

Where is it**?**

Concept introduced in Phonics/Language 2 Curriculum, lesson 49.

**Copy** the sentence; **add** the question mark.

1. Where did you go     Where did you go?

2. Was he ready on time

_____

_____ Was he ready on time? _____

_____

3. How did you do that

_____

_____ How did you do that? _____

_____

4. Who said that

_____

_____ Who said that? _____

_____

5. Will you play with me

_____

_____ Will you play with me? _____

_____

*Language Skills:* Identifying asking sentences (interrogative); ending an asking sentence with a question mark; reading sentences with comprehension; improving penmanship skills.

**Remember!**

Some sentences ask a question. They begin with a capital letter and end with a question mark.

**Write** these sentences correctly.

1. did you find it

   *Did you find it?*

2. who is calling me

   *Who is calling me?*

3. when did it happen

   *When did it happen?*

Can you match the words that mean almost the same? Optional

1. stool — chair
2. fast — quick
3. seashore — beach
4. forest — woods
5. cold — frozen

*Language Skills:* Ending an asking sentence with a question mark; beginning a sentence with a capital letter; identifying words having similar meanings.

*Language 2*   Lesson 53

A contraction is a short way of saying two words. We use an apostrophe to show where letters have been left out.     isn't = is not

Concept introduced in Phonics/Language 2 Curriculum, lesson 51.

**Match** the contraction with the two words it stands for.

| | | | | |
|---|---|---|---|---|
| 1. aren't | he is | | 6. it's | will not |
| 2. hadn't | was not | | 7. don't | you will |
| 3. he's | are not | | 8. won't | they have |
| 4. they're | had not | | 9. you'll | it is |
| 5. wasn't | they are | | 10. they've | do not |

**Write** these sentences correctly.

1. clocks tell us the time of day

_____

Clocks tell us the time of day.

_____

_____

2. honour thy father and mother

_____

Honour thy father and mother.

_____

_____

3. can you see him

_____

Can you see him?

**Language Skills:** Forming contractions; reading words and sentences with comprehension; recognizing that a telling sentence begins with a capital letter and ends with a period; recognizing that an asking sentence begins with a capital letter and ends with a question mark; improving penmanship skills.

**Match** the contraction with the two words it stands for.

1. can't       could not
2. couldn't     I am
3. hasn't      cannot
4. we've       has not
5. I'm        we have

6. I'll        he will
7. he'll       were not
8. isn't       you have
9. you've     is not
10. weren't     I will

**Write** a sentence with each word. Answers vary.

1. prize _____

_____

_____

2. trick _____

_____

_____

3. grape _____

_____

**Circle** a word to finish the sentence.

1. The crab can  (**walk**)  **swim**  on the sand.

2. The sea horse  (**looks**)  **walks**  like a horse with a tail.

3. Fish often  **heap** (**hide**)  in the dark shadows under

   the water.

4. The snail  **touches** (**carries**)  his home with him.

**Write** a word of opposite meaning for each word.  Answers vary.

**smile — frown**

1. you _____ me          4. over _____ under

2. down _____ up          5. walk _____ run

3. large _____ small       6. stop _____ go

**Circle** the phrase that matches the picture.

Jen's fish

Liz's pup

(Ann's crab)

Jon's box

(Jim's bike)

Jeff's ball

*Language Skills:* Demonstrating comprehension by choosing the correct word to complete a sentence; writing and spelling correctly a word of opposite meaning; reading for comprehension; identifying phrases that describe a picture.

A prefix is a letter or a group of letters added to the beginning of a root word.

sleep  (root word)
asleep  (prefix and root word)

Concept introduced in Phonics/Language 2 Curriculum, lesson 55.

**Add** the prefix a-. **Write** the word.

1. a cross     _across_

2. a like     _alike_

3. a lone     _alone_

4. a way     _away_

5. a while     _awhile_

6. a part     _apart_

**Write** three sentences about visiting a pond in the wintertime.
**Use** these words in the sentences.

| **frozen** | **frog** | **turtles** |

_Answers vary._

**Language Skills:** Forming words by adding the prefix _a_ to root words; using creative ability to write sentences including given words; recognizing that a sentence begins with a capital letter and ends with the proper punctuation mark.

**Add** the prefix a-, al-, or be- to the root word.  **Write** the word.

<u>be</u> long

1. _____belong or along_____

<u>be</u> side

4. _____beside or aside_____

<u>be</u> ware

2. _____beware or aware_____

<u>a</u> waken

5. _____awaken_____

<u>al</u> ways

3. _____always_____

<u>al</u> ready

6. _____already_____

**Rewrite** the sentences in the correct order.

1. is minnow fish small A a

_____A minnow is a small fish._____

2. long have tails Catfish

_____Catfish have long tails._____

3. pike A fish is thin a

_____A pike is a thin fish._____

4. fins have Goldfish orange

_____Goldfish have orange fins._____

**Language Skills:** Forming words by adding the prefixes *a, al,* or *be* to root words (help students choose the correct prefix); demonstrating comprehension by arranging words correctly to form a sentence; recognizing that a telling sentence begins with a capital letter and ends with a period; reading to learn facts.

58

Lesson 58    *Language 2*

**Read** the story.

## Billy and the Turtle

One sunny summer morning Tom Turtle hatched from an egg by the edge of the pond.  In a few days he learned to like the water.  Soon he was catching many fish and bugs to enjoy for his dinner.  Billy and his dog came to the pond one afternoon to play.  Billy threw stones, and he and his dog ran in and out of the water laughing and barking.  That scared Tom, so he pulled his head into his shell and pretended to sleep.  Tom was glad when he heard Billy's mom call him for dinner.

**Number** the sentences 1, 2, 3 to show what happened first, next, and last.

  2    Billy and his dog played at the pond.

  1    Tom was hatched from an egg.

  3    Billy's mom called him for dinner.

**Write** the picture word.  The rhyming words will help you.

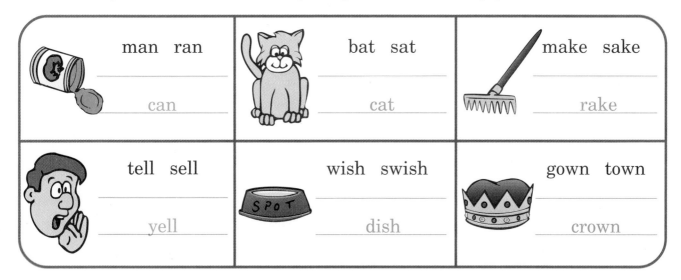

| man ran | bat sat | make sake |
|---|---|---|
| can | cat | rake |
| tell sell | wish swish | gown town |
| yell | dish | crown |

*Language Skills:* Identifying story sequence; reading a story with comprehension; analyzing words to form rhyming words; improving penmanship skills.

**Place** the correct punctuation at the end of each sentence.

1. We visited my uncle's pond on Wednesday.

2. Do you know what we saw?

3. My brother found six turtles and two frogs.

4. Can you guess how many turtles my sister found?

5. She had four turtles in her box.

6. Ed found a jar full of tadpoles.

7. I found a fat snail.

8. When can we visit the pond again?

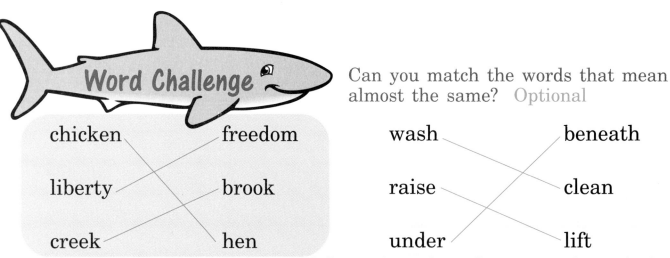

Word Challenge

Can you match the words that mean almost the same?  Optional

chicken    freedom
liberty    brook
creek    hen

wash    beneath
raise    clean
under    lift

*Language Skills:* Analyzing sentences to determine if telling or asking; ending a telling sentence with a period and an asking sentence with a question mark; identifying words with similar meanings; reading words and sentences with comprehension.

**Read** the question.   **Circle** the answer that is a sentence.

1. What kind of pet do you have?

One cat and one dog.

I have one cat and one dog.

2. What is your favorite kind of fish?

I like goldfish best of all.

Goldfish best of all.

3. What color is your cat?

My cat is black and white.

Black and white.

**Answer** each question with a complete sentence.   Answers vary.

1. What is your friend's name?

_____

_____

_____

2. What is your favorite color?

_____

_____

_____

3. Did you go fishing on vacation?

_____

_____

_____

**Circle** yes if the sentence is a question.  **Circle** no if it is not a question.
**Add** the correct punctuation.

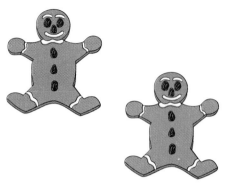

   (yes)  no   1. Why are you crying?

   (yes)  no   2. What can we eat?

   yes  (no)   3. I'm not sure.

   yes  (no)   4. I like to do this.

   (yes)  no   5. Do you want to go?

   yes  (no)   6. I know the answer.

   (yes)  no   7. Where is the teacher?

**Write** sentences using these words.  You will need to add some words of your own to make the sentences complete.  Answers vary.

1. October    leaves    fall

_____

_____

_____

2. November    pumpkins    orange

_____

_____

_____

*Language Skills:* Identifying asking sentences; using creative ability to write sentences including given words; recognizing that a telling sentence begins with a capital letter and ends with a period.

When a root word ends with a long vowel, a consonant, and a silent *e*, drop the *e* before adding a suffix that begins with a vowel.

hōpe̶ (root word)     hoped (suffix *-ed*)
hopes (suffix *-s*)     hoping (suffix *-ing*)

Concept introduced in Phonics/Language 2 Curriculum, lesson 61.

**Drop** the silent e and add the suffix -ed.  **Write** the word.

**bake̶ — baked**

1. save _____ saved          3. slope _____ sloped

2. rake _____ raked          4. stone _____ stoned

**Drop** the silent e and add the suffix -ing.  **Write** the word.

**bake̶ — baking**

1. save _____ saving          3. slope _____ sloping

2. rake _____ raking          4. stone _____ stoning

**Add** the suffix -s.  **Write** the word.

**bake — bakes**

1. save _____ saves          3. slope _____ slopes

2. rake _____ rakes          4. stone _____ stones

*Language Skills:* Forming words by adding the suffixes *ed, ing,* and *s* to root words that end with a long vowel, a consonant, and a silent *e;* improving penmanship skills.

**Add** the suffix -ing to these words.
**Write** the new word.

trade — trading

1. chase _____ chasing _____

2. ride _____ riding _____

3. hope _____ hoping _____

4. vote _____ voting _____

5. dive _____ diving _____

6. glide _____ gliding _____

7. shake _____ shaking _____

8. quake _____ quaking _____

9. like _____ liking _____

10. blaze _____ blazing _____

Word Challenge

Can you match the words that sound alike but have different meanings?
Optional

to          son
tale        two
sun         tail
road        rode

pain        see
hare        hair
meat        pane
sea         meet

*Language Skills:* Forming words by adding the suffix *ing* to root words; improving penmanship skills; identifying words that sound alike but have different spellings and meanings (homonyms).

Lesson 64    *Language 2*          64

Read the story.

## Moses Is Found

Baby Moses lay quietly in the special basket his mother had made to keep him safe in the Nile River.  She hid him there because she did not want to see her baby boy die as the Pharaoh said.  Sister Miriam watched him to see what would happen.  Suddenly the princess and her maids came near and heard the baby cry.  The princess loved Moses when she saw him and made him to be her own son.  But first she let Miriam go find someone to help care for Moses.  It was Moses' own mother!

Read each question.  Answer with a complete sentence.  Answers vary.

1. Why did Moses mother hide him in a basket?

2. Who watched over Moses in the river?

3. What did the princess hear when she came to the river?

*Language Skills:* Reading with comprehension to learn facts; demonstrating comprehension by answering questions correctly; recognizing that a telling sentence begins with a capital letter and ends with a period.

**Rewrite** each sentence with the correct capitalization and punctuation.

1. we have a swordtail fish in our tank at school

   We have a swordtail fish in our tank at school.

2. what kind of food should I feed the goldfish

   What kind of food should I feed the goldfish?

**Circle** the wrong word in each sentence. **Write** the correct word on the blank.

watching    pets    large    food

1. Small fish can be good ~~farmers.~~    **pets**

2. Ed enjoyed ~~walking~~ the guppies.    watching

3. Goldfish eat ~~fire~~ every day.    food

4. We had a ~~lazy~~ tank for ten fish.    large

*Language Skills:* Beginning a sentence with a capital letter; ending a telling sentence with a period and an asking sentence with a question mark; demonstrating comprehsion by identifying the wrong word in a sentence and choosing the word to correct the sentence.

**Circle** the correct punctuation mark.

1. Moses was hidden for three months   ?  (.)

2. Who was Moses' brother  (?)  .

3. Miriam was Moses' sister   ?  (.)

4. Where did Moses' mother hide him  (?)  .

5. Who found Baby Moses  (?)  .

6. The princess took Moses to the palace   ?  (.)

**Rewrite** each sentence so that it asks a question.  **Put** a ? at the end.

1. live you Where do

   Where do you live?

2. he did leave Why

   Why did he leave?

3. time is now it What

   What time is it now?

4. yesterday went town Who to

   Who went to town yesterday?

*Language Skills:* Ending a telling sentence with a period and an asking sentence with a question mark; demonstrating comprehension by arranging words correctly to form a sentence; reading to learn facts.

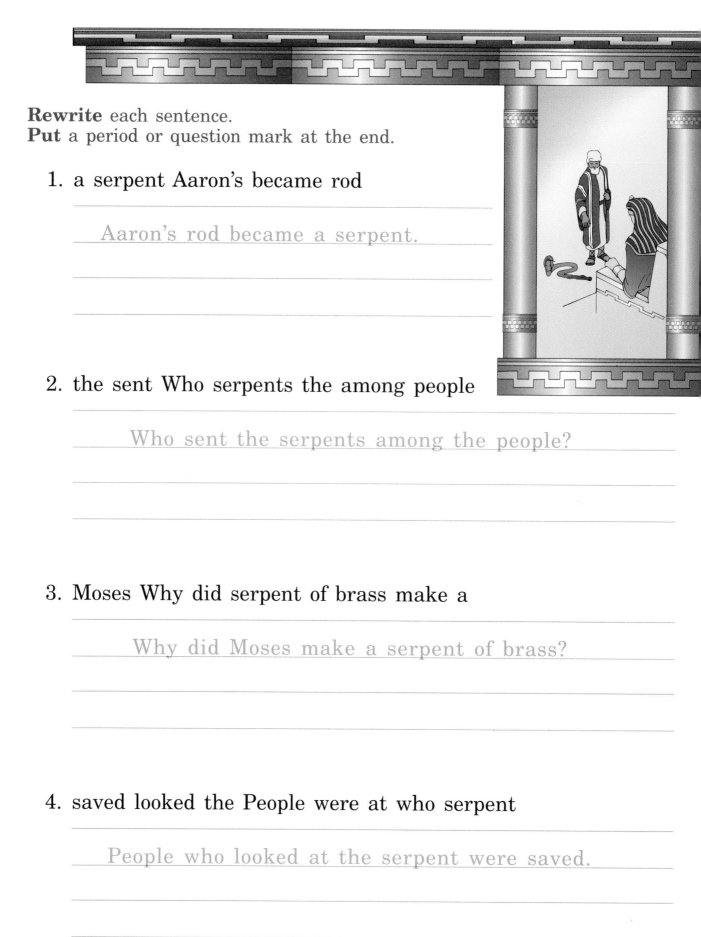

**Rewrite** each sentence.
**Put** a period or question mark at the end.

1. a serpent Aaron's became rod

   Aaron's rod became a serpent.

2. the sent Who serpents the among people

   Who sent the serpents among the people?

3. Moses Why did serpent of brass make a

   Why did Moses make a serpent of brass?

4. saved looked the People were at who serpent

   People who looked at the serpent were saved.

*Language Skills:* Demonstrating comprehension by arranging words correctly to form a sentence; ending a telling sentence with a period and an asking sentence with a question mark; improving penmanship skills.

Lesson 68   *Language 2*                    68

**Match** to make compound words.

| | | | | | | |
|---|---|---|---|---|---|---|
| 1. honey | | father | | 5. butter | | car |
| 2. top | | bee | | 6. road | | fly |
| 3. base | | ball | | 7. street | | self |
| 4. grand | | coat | | 8. him | | side |

**Write** sentences making questions.  Answers vary.

1. How     **How are you today?**

 

2. When

 

 

3. Where

 

 

4. How much

 

 

5. Why

 

*Language Skills:* Forming compound words; using creative ability to write questions when the first word is given; ending an asking sentence with a question mark; improving penmanship skills.

Sentences start with capital letters. Names of months and days of the week always start with a capital letter.

My birthday is on Monday, July 30.

**Circle** the letters that need a capital letter in each sentence.

1. our school will start on the last monday in august.

2. in march we will move to New Jersey.

3. it will snow sometime in january.

4. on wednesday, november 4th, I was sick.

5. my birthday is on tuesday, april 6th, this year.

**Answer** the questions in two sentences. Answers vary.

1. When is your birthday? What do you want for your birthday?

_____

_____

_____

2. What is your favorite month? Why do you like it?

_____

_____

_____

_____

*Language Skills:* Capitalizing the names of the months and days of the week; capitalizing the first word in a sentence; answering questions with a sentence; ending a telling sentence with a period.

Lesson 70   *Language 2*                    70

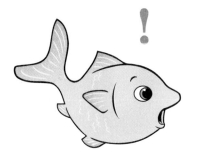

A sentence that shows surprise, fear, or excitement begins with a capital letter and ends with an exclamation point.

What a wonderful day!
Ouch, it hurts!

Concept introduced in Phonics/Language 2 Curriculum, lesson 69.

**Place** an exclamation point at the end of each sentence.

1. Help, I can't get out!

2. I found it!

3. Linda, look out!

4. Wow, that is great!

**Place** the correct punctuation at the end of each sentence.
**Use** a period, a question mark, or an exclamation point.

1. I went for a long walk.

2. Did you find out the answer?

3. Look how happy he is!

4. God said it; I believe it.

5. How can we know the way?

6. What a smart girl!

7. May we go, too?

8. Oh, it hurts!

**Language Skills:** Identifying exclamatory sentences; ending an exclamatory sentence with an exclamation point; analyzing sentences to determine what type; placing the proper punctuation at the end of a sentence; reading sentences with comprehension.

71

**Circle** the correct punctuation.

1. Oh look, a new toy    ?    .    (!)

2. What is the answer    (?)    .    !

3. I love to go to the fair    ?    (.) (!)
   *or*

4. There are three snails on the trail    ?    (.)    !

5. Keep away from the bear cage    ?    .    (!)

6. The snakes are in the box    ?    (.)    !

7. Help!   One snake got out    ?    .    (!)

8. May I go with you    (?)    .    !

**Use** these words to write sentences that show surprise, fear, or excitement.

Help    1. _____ Answers vary. _____

_____

_____

Ouch    2. _____

_____

_____

What    3. _____

_____

***Language Skills:*** Demonstrating comprehension by choosing the proper end punctuation mark; using creative ability to write exclamatory sentences including a given word; recognizing that an exclamatory sentence begins with a capital letter and ends with an exclamation point.

Lesson 72   *Language 2*

72

When a root word ends with a consonant and *y*, change the *y* to an *i* before adding the suffix beginning with an *e*.

funny  (root word)
funnier  (suffix *-er*)
funniest  (suffix *-est*)

Concept introduced in Phonics/Language 2 Curriculum, lesson 71.

**Change** the y to i, and then add a suffix.  Answers vary.

 -ed   -er   -en   -es   -est

**lady — ladies**

1. baby _____ babies _____
2. try _____ tried _____
3. marry _____ married _____

4. tidy _____ tidiest _____
5. pry _____ pried _____
6. cry _____ crier _____

**Put** in the marks of punctuation.
There are two sentences in each line.

1. Seaweed is a water plant.  It is easy to get.

2. Seaweed does not have roots.  Do you know why?

3. It holds fast to rocks.  Some seaweed is small.

4. Seaweed has several colors.  They are beautiful.

*Language Skills:* Forming words by adding a suffix beginning with an *e* to root words ending with a consonant and *y*; demonstrating comprehension by choosing the correct end punctuation marks; reading to learn facts.

**Change** the y to i; **add** a suffix. Answers vary.

-ed -er -en -es -est

lazy — lazier

1. happy    happiest          4. pretty    prettiest

2. shabby   shabbier          5. crazy     crazier

3. penny    pennies           6. sleepy    sleepiest

**Write** yes if the sentence is written correctly.
**Write** no if the sentence is not written correctly.

no    1. Did you know that sand dollars are also called
         sea cookies.

no    2. Living sand dollars are brown or purple in color?

no    3. inside the sand dollar are five white teeth that
         look like doves!

yes   4. The spines on the outside of a sand dollar are
         sharp.

yes   5. Ouch, I stepped on one!

yes   6. Sam has a collection of sand dollars.

no    7. His sand dollars are beautiful?

*Language Skills:* Forming words by adding a suffix beginning with an *e* to root words ending with a consonant and y; analyzing sentences to determine if written correctly; reading sentences with comprehension; reading to learn facts.

**Circle** the letters that need to be capitals.
**Add** the punctuation marks.
**Write** the sentences on the lines.

1. (t)his is a book about jellyfish.

   This is a book about jellyfish.

2. (w)ow, this one is big!

   Wow, this one is big!

3. (h)ow long do jellyfish live?

   How long do jellyfish live?

4. (j)ellyfish live about one year.

   Jellyfish live about one year.

5. (h)elp, one jellyfish stung me!

   Help, one jellyfish stung me!

*Language Skills:* Recognizing that sentences begin with a capital letter and end with the proper punctuation mark; demonstrating comprehension by choosing the proper end punctuation mark; improving penmanship skills.

Circle the letters that need to be capital letters.
Put a period or question mark at the end of each sentence.

1. the month after october is november.

2. what is your favorite day in december?

3. our school will get out on monday, may 30.

4. is that the last friday of february?

5. how many sundays are there in april?

Find the special message the fish has for you.
Color the circle if you used that letter as a capital above.

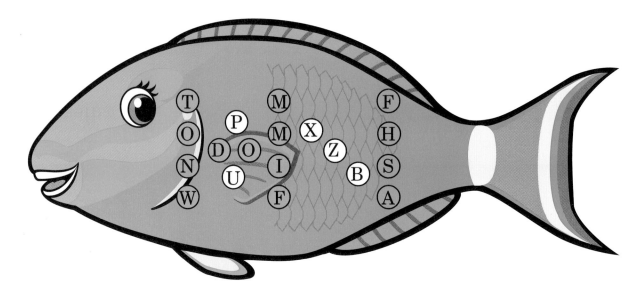

Write two or three sentences telling what you ate for dinner last night
and how it tasted.

_____

_____

_____

_____

_____

*Language Skills:* Capitalizing the names of the months and days of the week and the first word in a sentence; ending a
sentence with the proper punctuation; reading sentences with comprehension; using creative ability to write sentences.

Lesson 76    *Language 2*                    76

**Add** the suffix -ing.  **Write** the word.

**hide — hiding**

1. bite

   _biting_

2. dive

   _diving_

3. make

   _making_

4. rope

   _roping_

5. take

   _taking_

6. rule

   _ruling_

**Write** four sentences about what you do to get ready for school each morning.

**Early in the Morning**

_Answers vary._

*Language Skills:* Forming words by adding the suffix *ing* to root words; using creative ability to write a story; recognizing that a sentence begins with a capital letter and ends with the proper punctuation mark.

**Add** the suffix -ed.  **Write** the word.

1. bake

    _baked_

2. fade

    _faded_

3. gaze

    _gazed_

4. hope

    _hoped_

5. time

    _timed_

6. wade

    _waded_

**Write** four sentences about what you do before bed each night.

**Just before Bed**

_Answers vary._

*Language Skills:* Forming words by adding the suffix *ed* to root words; using creative ability to write a story; recognizing that a sentence begins with a capital letter and ends with the proper punctuation mark.

## Word Challenge

Can you match the words that mean almost the same? Optional

1. cut          fast

2. speedy       boss

3. leader       say

4. speak        tear

5. small        dinner

6. supper       save

7. hurry        rush

8. keep         tiny

**Write** three interesting sentences about how you could surprise your family.

### A Surprise for My Family

Answers vary.

*Language Skills:* Identifying words that have similar meanings; using creative ability to write sentences; recognizing that a sentence begins with a capital letter and ends with the proper punctuation mark.

79

**Write** a thank you note for one of your Christmas gifts.

Students may recopy their note onto p. 171, address it, and mail it.

Dear _____,

Thank you very much for _____

_____

_____

I really like _____

_____

_____

Christmas is my favorite holiday because _____

_____

_____

_____

Love,

_____

_____

*Language Skills:* Using creative ability to write a thank you note; recognizing that a telling sentence begins with a capital letter and usually ends with a period; improving penmanship skills.

Lesson 80    Language 2

Write the prefix en- or un- on the blank.

**un**button

1. __en__ circle     3. __en__ case     5. __un__ leash

2. __en__ camp     4. __un__ just     6. __un__ wrap

Write th_____ which matches the definition.

_____le_____ form a circle around

___encamp___ settle in tents for a time

3. ___encase___ close, cover completely

4. ___unjust___ not fair

5. ___unleash___ let loose

6. ___unwrap___ open, take off covering

Write two sentences using these words. **Moses**    **encamp**    **Ark**

Answers vary.

*Language Skills:* Forming words by adding the prefixes *en* or *un* to root words (help students choose the correct prefix); demonstrating vocabulary skill by matching words and definitions; using creative ability to write sentences including given words; recognizing that a sentence begins with a    capital letter and ends with the proper punctuation mark.

*Language 2*    Lesson 81

Use the words in the picture to finish the story.

five
beak
crabs
crane
water

A whooping ___crane___ is a large, white bird that lives

by the ___water___. He stands almost ___five___ feet

tall and weighs about twenty-five pounds. He has a long, pointed

___beak___. He eats small fish, shrimp, and ___crabs___.

Answer the questions in complete sentences. Answers vary.

1. What is the name of the bird in the picture?

___

___

___

2. What color is the bird?

___

___

___

3. What does he eat?

___

___

___

Language Skills: Demonstrating comprehension by choosing the correct word to complete a sentence; reading to learn facts; answering questions in a sentence; recognizing that a telling sentence begins with a capital letter and ends with a period.

*Sit* means "to rest" or "to be seated." The word *sat* is used to tell about something that has already happened.

Sue will *sit* in the chair.
Ann *sat* down on the step.

Concept introduced in Phonics/Language 2 Curriculum, lesson 81.

**Write** sit or sat on the lines.

1. We should _____sit_____ with good posture in our chair.

2. Ellen _____sat_____ down to write a letter.

3. Angie will _____sit_____ on the swing while Karen pushes her.

4. Steve _____sat_____ on the steps waiting for the postman to come.

5. Children should _____sit_____ still in church.

6. _____Sit_____ still or the photograph will not be good.

**Write** two sentences using sit or sat.

1. _____Answers vary._____

2. _____

***Language Skills:*** Using *sit* and *sat* correctly; demonstrating reading comprehension by choosing the correct word to complete a sentence; using creative ability to write sentences; recognizing that a sentence begins with a capital letter and ends with the proper punctuation mark.

*Language 2*   Lesson 83

> **Set** means "to put or place something."
> Mother *set* the dishes on the table.

Concept introduced in Phonics/Language 2 Curriculum, lesson 81.

**Write** set on the lines.

1. Judy, will you please ___set___ the table?

2. ___Set___ all your books on your desk.

3. Connie ___set___ the picture on the shelf.

**Write** one sentence using set.

_____

_____ Answers vary. _____

**Underline** the correct word in each sentence.

1. Boaz (sit, <u>sat</u>, set) at the city gates.

2. Gideon (sit, sat, <u>set</u>) up a sacrifice to the Lord.

3. Jesus (sit, <u>sat</u>, set) in the boat and talked to the people.

4. Gideon (sit, sat, <u>set</u>) out a fleece to the Lord.

5. (<u>Sit</u>, Sat, Set) here and wait.

6. (Sit, Sat, <u>Set</u>) your book on the library desk.

*Language Skills:* Using *sit, sat,* and *set* correctly; demonstrating reading comprehension and choosing the correct word to complete a sentence; using creative ability to write a sentence; recognizing that a sentence begins with a capital letter and ends with the proper punctuation mark.

Lesson 84  *Language 2*  84

ABC order, or alphabetical order, means to arrange things in the order of the alphabet.

| antlers | — In | candle | — Not in |
|---------|------|--------|----------|
| barrel | ABC | antlers | ABC |
| candle | order | barrel | order |
| door | | door | |

Concept introduced in Phonics/Language 2 Curriculum, lesson 44.

**Arrange** these words in ABC order.

crow    ant    duck    bee

1. ____ant____

2. ____bee____

3. ____crow____

4. ____duck____

fox    gull    elephant    horse

1. ____elephant____

2. ____fox____

3. ____gull____

4. ____horse____

**Read** the sentences.  **Write** the word to complete each sentence.

swim    birds    eggs

1. Penguins are black and white ____birds____.

2. Penguins can walk, ____swim____, or slide.

3. They lay one or two ____eggs____ each year.

**Language Skills:** Alphabetizing—preparation for using the dictionary; demonstrating comprehension by choosing the correct word to complete a sentence; reading to learn facts.

**Read** the sentences.
**Number** them as they happen.

## Penguins

___3___ The baby penguins hatch, and the parents feed them sea-food.

___1___ Penguins live in the snow and cold lands of the world.

___2___ The mother penguin lays one or two eggs.

___4___ The babies learn to swim and fish by themselves.

**Divide** the words between two consonants that are alike.
**Write** the number of syllables in each word.

c o p|p e r – 2     t u n|n e l – 2     y e l|l o w – 2     s u m|m e r – 2

**Arrange** these words in ABC order.

| **monkey** **walrus** **raccoon** **lobster** | | **opossum** **tiger** **donkey** **penguin** | |
|---|---|---|---|
| 1. | lobster | 1. | donkey |
| 2. | monkey | 2. | opossum |
| 3. | raccoon | 3. | penguin |
| 4. | walrus | 4. | tiger |

*Language Skills:* Recognizing sequential order; reading sentences with comprehension; syllabicating and determining the number of syllables in a word; alphabetizing—preparation for using the dictionary.

**Arrange** these words in ABC order.

| | | | |
|---|---|---|---|
| 1. yellow | robin | 1. X-ray | quail |
| 2. walrus | seal | 2. quail | tepee |
| 3. robin | umbrella | 3. zero | vane |
| 4. umbrella | walrus | 4. vane | X-ray |
| 5. seal | yellow | 5. tepee | zero |

**Answer** each question with a complete sentence.
Answers vary.

1. Who made the heavens and the earth?

2. From what does Jesus save us?

3. Why did Jesus die on the cross?

*Language Skills:* Alphabetizing—preparation for using the dictionary; answering questions in sentences; recognizing that a telling sentence begins with a capital letter and ends with a period.

> *Too* means "also" or "more than enough."
> *Two* means the number 2.
> For most other meanings, use *to*.
>
>   I want to go, *too*.
>   I need *two* pencils.
>   I went *to* the store.

Concept introduced in Phonics/Language 2 Curriculum, lesson 86.

**Finish** the sentences with too, two, or to.

1. Becky went with **two** girls **to** the fair.

2. The _two_ horses were caught, _too_ .

3. Tom sent _two_ letters _to_ his cousin.

4. Mother went _to_ town and bought _two_ sacks of groceries.

5. Susan was _too_ frightened _to_ scream.

**Write** three sentences using too, two, or to. Answers vary.

1. _____

_____

2. _____

_____

3. _____

**Language Skills:** Using *too, two,* and *to* correctly, demonstrating reading comprehension by choosing the correct word to complete a sentence; using creative ability to write sentences; recognizing that a sentence begins with a capital letter and ends with the proper punctuation mark.

Lesson 88    Language 2                                          88

**Circle** the letters that need to be capitals.
**Put** the punctuation at the end of the sentence.

1. sandy will feed her pet porcupine.

2. susan, what are you doing?

3. help, I lost it!

4. did robin find her pet spider?

5. tuesday we went to the circus.

6. what fun we had!

7. january is a cold winter month.

8. god made the snowflakes for us to enjoy.

**Write** 3 or 4 sentences about pets you might see at a pet store.

_____

_____

_____

_____

_____

_____

*Language Skills:* Recognizing that sentences begin with a capital letter and end with the proper punctuation mark; demonstrating comprehension by choosing the proper end punctuation; using creative ability to write sentences.

*Language 2*  Lesson 89

**Write** a story about a pet show. The words might help you.

Title

dogs      guinea pigs

cats      spiders

birds      iguanas

fish      hamsters

gerbils      rabbits

most obedient

most faithful

most unusual

most beautiful

*Language Skills:* Using creative ability to write a story; recognizing that a telling sentence begins with a capital letter and ends with appropriate punctuation; improving penmanship skills.

**Remember!**

*Too* means "also" or "more than enough." *Two* means the number 2. For most other meanings, use *to*.

**Write** yes on the blank if the sentence is correct.
**Write** no if it is incorrect.

___no___    1. The water is two deep to swim in.

___no___    2. The two boys went too the shore.

___yes___    3. Joe was too scared to move.

___no___    4. Lynn sang to special songs in church.

___yes___    5. Don missed too many questions on the two tests.

___yes___    6. We need to thank God every day.

**Circle** the correct word in each sentence.

1. Where do you  (sat, (sit), set)  in school?

2. Sherry wants  (two, (to), too)  go to the beach.

3. Helen was  (two, to, (too))  sleepy to talk.

4. I will  ((set), sat, sit)  the pan on the stove.

5. Jerry had  (too, to, (two))  pails of berries.

6. The birds  ((sit), (sat), set)  on the clothesline.
                or

*Language Skills:* Using *too, two,* and *to* correctly; using *sat, sit,* and *set* correctly; analyzing sentences to decide if correct; demonstrating reading comprehension by choosing the correct word to complete the sentence.

When arranging words in ABC order, if the first letter is the same, look at the second letter. If the second letter is the same, look at the third letter.

| | |
|---|---|
| bat | bread |
| bell | bring |
| bus | brought |

**Arrange** these words in ABC order.

| drop | dive | dust | | church | checks | child |
|---|---|---|---|---|---|---|

1. _____dive_____          1. _____checks_____

2. _____drop_____          2. _____child_____

3. _____dust_____          3. _____church_____

**Write** four interesting sentences that tell how to build a snowman.

## How to Build the Biggest Snowman

Answers vary.

*Language Skills:* Alphabetizing preparation for using the dictionary; using creative ability to write instructions; recognizing that a telling sentence begins with a capital letter and ends with a period.

Concept is
introduced in
Phonics/
Language 2
Curriculum
in lesson 91.

*May* is used to ask or give permission.
*Can* is used to show ability or power.

*May* I go to the store?
He *can* do a good job.

**Write** may or can on the lines.

1. Dad, _____ *may* _____ we go to the store now?

2. Yes, you _____ *may* _____ go right now.

3. _____ *Can* _____ you tell me who is ready?

4. _____ *May* _____ I have that job?

5. God _____ *can* _____ do anything.

6. My sister said I _____ *may* _____ go with them.

**Write** two sentences with may or can.  Answers vary.

1. _____

_____

2. _____

*Language Skills:* Using *may* or *can*; demonstrating comprehension by choosing the correct word to complete a
sentence; using creative ability to write sentences; recognizing that a sentence begins with a capital letter and ends
with the proper punctuation mark.

93

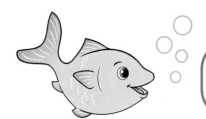

**Circle** the correct word in parentheses.

1. (May, Can)  I go outside now?

2. You  (may, can)  wear your new suit.

3. Ed  (may, can)  go to Bill's house.

4. Wendy  (can, may)  hear the wind blow.

5. Alan  (may, can)  speak well for only being
   (two, to, too)  years old.

6. Sue  (may, can)  (sit, set, sat)  very still for the artist.

7. We  (may, can)  pray  (too, to, two)  God every day.

8. Joy  (sit, set, sat)  down  (to, two, too)  read
   (to, two, too)  the children.

**Write** three sentences about the most beautiful flower you have ever seen.
**Describe** its color, shape, and size.

Answers vary.

*Language Skills:* Using *may* or *can*; using *to, too,* or *two*; using *sit, sat, set*; demonstrating reading comprehension by choosing the correct word to complete a sentence; using creative ability to write sentences; recognizing that a sentence begins with a capital letter and ends with the proper punctuation mark.

Lesson 94    *Language 2*                    94

*Remember!*

A sentence is a complete thought.

**Circle** yes if the sentence is complete.  **Circle** no if the sentence is not complete.  **Put** in the punctuation if the sentence is complete.

(yes) no 1. The cat jumped down from the chair.

(yes) no 2. Dan, look at that.

(yes) no 3. How many cats do you have?

yes (no) 4. After that Randy

(yes) no 5. Dogs can bark.

yes (no) 6. I would like to have a

yes (no) 7. Sunday is a good day for

(yes) no 8. Did you see that trick?

**Arrange** these words in ABC order.

| **r**ain   **l**ightning   **t**hunder | | **ha**nd   **ha**il   **ha**ve |
|---|---|---|

1. _____ lightning _____     1. _____ hail _____

2. _____ rain _____     2. _____ hand _____

3. _____ thunder _____     3. _____ have _____

*Language Skills:* Analyzing groups of words to determine if a sentence; demonstrating comprehension by choosing the correct end punctuation mark; alphabetizing—preparation for using the dictionary.

## Dolphins

A dolphin lives in the water but it is not a fish. It breathes air through a hole in the top of its head. It eats fish with its 100 teeth! A dolphin can see and hear very well, so this protects it from its enemy, the shark.

A group of dolphins is called a school. All dolphins stay in the school and help each other. The mother dolphins protect the babies. The father dolphins teach the babies how to obey. Sometimes a father has to spank its baby by biting its tail. Ouch!

**Mark** the ○ beside the correct answer.

1. Who is the dolphin's enemy?
   - ○ whale
   - ◉ shark
   - ○ fish

2. What does a dolphin use to protect itself from its enemy?
   - ○ hole on its head
   - ○ 100 teeth
   - ◉ eyes and ears

3. How does a dolphin breathe?
   - ○ through its mouth
   - ○ through its gills
   - ◉ through a hole on its head

4. Why does the father bite the baby's tail?
   - ○ for affection
   - ◉ for punishment
   - ○ for protection

*Language Skills:* Reading with comprehension to learn facts; demonstrating comprehension by answering questions correctly.

**Draw** a line to the part that finishes the sentence.

1. Moses was chosen      were spies in the promised land.

2. Joshua and Caleb      by God.

3. Rahab hid      fell down.

4. God promised      two men in her house.

5. The walls of Jericho      a victory.

**Describe** in four sentences what you will see as you go home from school today.

**Going Home**

Answers vary.

**Language Skills:** Demonstrating comprehension by matching the end of a sentence with the beginning; using creative ability to write about the familiar; recognizing that a sentence begins with a capital letter and ends with the proper punctuation mark.

Concept is
introduced in
Phonics/
Language 2
Curriculum in
lesson 96.

> *Teach* means "to give knowledge."
> *Learn* means "to get knowledge."
> Miss Lee will *teach* the class today.
> The class will *learn* to listen.

**Write** teach or learn on the lines.

1. A baby will _____learn_____ to walk when he is about eleven months old.

2. Miss Brown will _____teach_____ us how to speak in Spanish.

3. I can _____teach_____ my brother how to ride a bike.

4. Helen will _____learn_____ her Bible verse by tomorrow.

**Write** one sentence with teach and one sentence with learn.

_____

_____Answers vary._____

_____

_____

**Circle** the correct answer.

1. (Sit, (Set))  means "to put or place something."

2. ((Too), To)  means "also" or "more than enough."

3. ((May), Can)  is used to ask or give permission.

***Language Skills:*** Using *teach* and *learn*; using *sit, sat,* and *set*; using *to, too,* and *two*; using *may* and *can*; demonstrating comprehension by choosing the correct word to complete a sentence; using creative ability to write a sentence; recognizing that a sentence begins with a capital letter and ends with the proper punctuation mark.

Circle the word that means the opposite of the word in the box.

| 1. short | 2. good | 3. open | 4. loudly |
|---|---|---|---|
| fat | look | (close) | quickly |
| (long) | see | watch | (softly) |
| small | (bad) | inside | easily |
| 5. rich | 6. new | 7. weak | 8. light |
| power | (old) | good | (dark) |
| such | slew | sneak | fright |
| (poor) | gold | (strong) | day |

Write two sentences telling how Don will play with his new train.

**Don's Train**

Answers vary.

railroad
engineer
station
tracks
locomotive
tunnel
whistle

**Write** about the day your toy train became real and you were the engineer.

## My Train Ride

Answers vary.

*Language Skills:* Using creative ability to write a story; recognizing that a sentence begins with a capital letter and ends with the proper punctuation mark; improving penmanship skills.

Lesson 100   *Language 2*
100

**Remember!**

*Teach* means "to give knowledge."
*Learn* means "to get knowledge."

**Circle** the correct word in parentheses.

1. Cindy could (teach, (learn)) to count by using pencils.

2. Bob wanted to ((teach), learn) Dick how to swim.

3. Paul will (learn, (teach)) his dog some new tricks.

4. ((May), Can) we go to the zoo tomorrow?

5. ((Can), May) you name the four Gospels?

6. Jeff will get (too, (two)) chances to answer the question.

7. The kitten was ((too), to) frightened to run away from the dog.

8. Ben ((sat), set) on the back steps.

9. Barb will ((set), sit) the table for us.

**Write** three sentences about the time you found a starfish.
**Tell** what you did with it.

Answers vary.

**Language Skills:** Using *teach* and *learn;* using *sit, sat,* and *set;* using *to, too,* and *two;* using *may* and *can;* demonstrating comprehension by choosing the correct word to complete a sentence; using creative ability to write a sentence; recognizing that a sentence begins with a capital letter and ends with the proper punctuation mark.

 *Language 2* Lesson 101

**Circle** the letters that need to be capitalized.
**Put** in the punctuation.

1. (a)braham Lincoln grew up in a log cabin.

2. (w)e celebrate his birthday on (f)ebruary 12.

3. (y)oung Abe was an honest, hardworking lawyer.

4. (d)id you know he was against slavery?

5. (l)incoln was President during the War between the States.

6. (a)mericans built the Lincoln Memorial to honor Lincoln.

**Arrange** these words in ABC order.

| Bible | patriotic | country | flag | God | American |
|-------|-----------|---------|------|-----|----------|

1. _____American_____

2. _____Bible_____

3. _____country_____

4. _____flag_____

5. _____God_____

6. _____patriotic_____

*Language Skills:* Reading with comprehension to learn facts; capitalizing the months of the year and the first word in the sentence; ending a sentence with the correct punctuation mark; alphabetizing—preparation for using the dictionary.

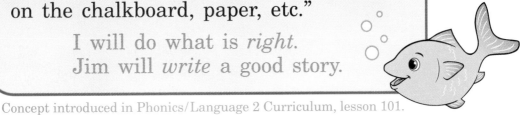

*Right* means "correct" or "true."
*Write* means "to put words or numbers on the chalkboard, paper, etc."
I will do what is *right*.
Jim will *write* a good story.

Concept introduced in Phonics/Language 2 Curriculum, lesson 101.

**Write** *right* or *write* on the lines.

1. Anna could not find the _____right_____ page in her math book.

2. My brother can _____write_____ the color words in Spanish.

3. Will you _____write_____ to me while I am gone?

4. Tim spelled every word _____right_____ on his test.

**Write** one sentence with *right* and one sentence with *write*.

_____Answers vary._____

**Language Skills:** Using *right* and *write;* demonstrating comprehension by choosing the correct word to complete a sentence; using creative ability to write sentences; recognizing that a sentence begins with a capital letter and ends with the proper punctuation mark.

**Write** four sentences about something beautiful you have seen in America.
**Tell** what it looks like and why you like it.

Answers vary.

**Circle** the correct answer for each sentence.

1. (Too, Two)  means the number 2.

2. (Sit, Set)  means "to rest" or "to be seated."

3. (May, Can)  is used to show ability or power.

4. (Teach, Learn)  means "to give knowledge."

5. (Right, Write)  means "correct" or "true."

*Language Skills:* Using creative ability to write sentences; recognizing that a sentence begins with a capital letter and ends with the proper punctuation mark. Using *two* and *too;* using *sit* and *set;* using *may* and *can;* using *teach* and *learn;* using *right* and *write.*

Lesson 104    *Language 2*

104

worship God     do right           honest     helpful
freedom         Independence Day     fair       friendly
Thanksgiving                                kind
Christmas

**Write** a story about why you love America.

Title

*Language Skills:* Using creative ability to write a story; recognizing that a sentence begins with a capital letter and ends with the appropriate punctuation; improving penmanship skills.

## ★ The Liberty Bell ★

A symbol of American freedom is the Liberty Bell. It weighs 2,080 pounds and is about 3 feet high. Many years ago the bell was rung to call the people together, or to tell the death of a great leader. It has these words on it: "Proclaim Liberty throughout the land unto all the inhabitants thereof." —*Leviticus 25:10*

**Mark** the ○ beside the best answer.

1. The Liberty Bell is . . .

   ○ very light
   ◉ very heavy
   ○ very new

2. How tall is the Liberty Bell?

   ○ a foot
   ○ a mile
   ◉ a yard

**Write** the answers to the questions in complete sentences. Answers vary.

1. What is liberty?

   _____

   _____

   _____

   _____

2. Name two reasons why the Liberty Bell is important to you.

   _____

   _____

   _____

*Language Skills:* Reading with comprehension to learn facts; demonstrating comprehension by answering questions correctly; recognizing that a telling sentence begins with a capital letter and ends with a period.

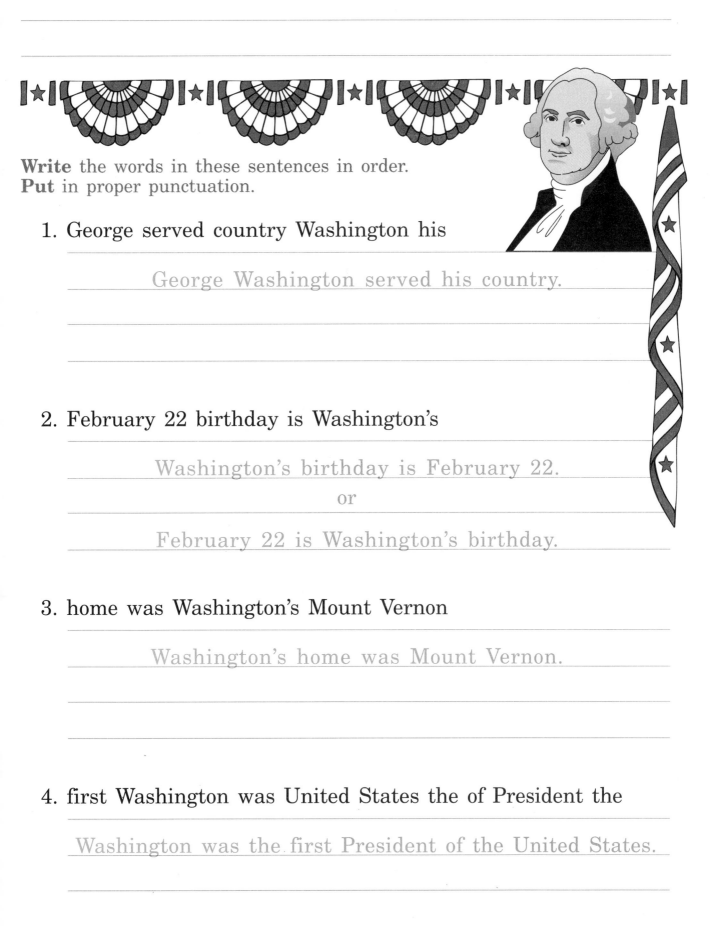

**Write** the words in these sentences in order.
**Put** in proper punctuation.

1. George served country Washington his

   George Washington served his country.

2. February 22 birthday is Washington's

   Washington's birthday is February 22.

   or

   February 22 is Washington's birthday.

3. home was Washington's Mount Vernon

   Washington's home was Mount Vernon.

4. first Washington was United States the of President the

   Washington was the first President of the United States.

*Language Skills:* Demonstrating comprehension by arranging words of a sentence in proper order; reading to learn facts; ending a telling sentence with a period; improving penmanship skills.

     *Language 2*   Lesson 107

Singular means one, and plural means more than one.

cat    (singular)
cats   (plural)

Concept introduced in Phonics/Language 2 Curriculum, lesson 106.

**Add** -s to make these words plural.  **Write** the word.

## dog — dogs

1. duck _____ ducks

2. bug _____ bugs

3. bee _____ bees

4. sack _____ sacks

5. sail _____ sails

6. egg _____ eggs

**Divide** the words between two consonants that are *not* alike.
**Write** how many syllables are in each word.

1. s p r o u t ___1___

2. b a r n | y a r d ___2___

3. d u c k | l i n g ___2___

4. b i r t h | d a y ___2___

5. b r a n c h ___1___

6. c a r | p e n | t e r ___3___

7. w h i r l | w i n d ___2___

8. n a p | k i n ___2___

**Write** a question to your teacher.

_____

Answers vary.

_____

_____

*Language Skills:* Pluralizing words by adding *s;* syllabicating and determining the number of syllables in a word; using creative ability to write a question; recognizing that an asking sentence begins with a capital letter and ends with a question mark.

**Read** the story.

## Our Flag

Our flag is a symbol of freedom. Our flag is red, white, and blue. Red stands for courage or bravery. White stands for purity. Blue stands for truth and loyalty.

Each of the 50 stars represents a state in the United States. The 13 stripes help us to remember that we began with only 13 states. There are 7 red stripes and 6 white stripes.

**Finish** the sentences.

1. Our flag has _____50_____ stars.

2. Our flag has _____13_____ stripes.

3. Our flag has _____7_____ red stripes.

4. Our flag has _____6_____ white stripes.

5. Red stands for _____courage (bravery)_____.

6. White stands for _____purity_____.

7. Blue stands for _____truth_____ and _____loyalty_____.

**Language Skills:** Reading with comprehension to learn facts; demonstrating comprehension by filling in the blanks correctly.

**Write** a story about our flag.

Title

beautiful
courage
bravery
purity
truth
loyalty
50 stars
13 stripes
7 red stripes
6 white stripes

*Language Skills:* Using creative ability to write a story; recognizing that a sentence begins with a capital letter and ends with the proper punctuation mark.

Lesson 110   *Language 2*                    110

**Remember!**

Singular means one, and plural means more than one.

**Add** -s to make these words plural.  **Write** the word.

1. dog    dogs

2. mule    mules

3. stamp    stamps

4. frog    frogs

5. flag    flags

6. goat    goats

7. brick    bricks

8. clock    clocks

**Make** compound words.  Answers vary.

**rain — rainbow**

1. bed    bedtime

2. base    baseball

3. her    herself

4. milk    milkman

5. cup    cupcake

6. sun    sunshine

**Write** a sentence using one compound word.  Answers vary.

_____

**Language Skills:** Pluralizing words by adding *s;* forming compound words; using creative ability to write a sentence including a compound word; recognizing that a sentence begins with a capital letter and ends with the proper punctuation mark.

 *Language 2*    Lesson 111

**Match** the two words to the contraction.

1. should have      could've
2. she will      should've
3. could have      she'll

4. should not      haven't
5. she is      shouldn't
6. have not      she's

## ★ Statue of Liberty ★

The Statue of Liberty was a gift from France to America to celebrate our 100th birthday as a free country. The Liberty Lady holds a tablet which stands for the Declaration of Independence in one hand and a torch in the other hand. She stands on an island in New York harbor and welcomes people to our free land.

**Answer** the questions about the story in complete sentences.   Answers vary.

1. Where did America get the Statue of Liberty?

2. What does the Liberty Lady hold in her hands?

3. Where is the Statue of Liberty?

*Language Skills:* Forming contractions; reading with comprehension to learn facts; demonstrating comprehension by answering questions correctly; recognizing that a telling sentence begins with a capital letter and ends with a period.

> *Blue* is a color.
>
> *Blew* means "moved, usually by air."
>
> Clouds floated across the *blue* sky.
> Sandy *blew* out the candles.

Concept introduced in Phonics/Language 2 Curriculum, lesson 111.

**Write** blue or blew on the lines.

1. The door ___blew___ open during the storm.

2. Dad bought Todd a ___blue___ suit.

3. The wolf ___blew___ and ___blew___, but he could not blow down the brick house.

4. My aunt's baby has ___blue___ eyes.

**Write** two sentences with blue or blew.

___Answers vary.___

___

**Circle** the correct word in parentheses.

1. (May, Can)  I wear my  (blew, blue)  dress  (two, to)  church?

2. Lynn will  (set, sit)  still while she  (learns, teaches)  to  (right, write)  the letter *q*.

**Language Skills:** Using *may* and *can*; using *blew* and *blue*; using *two* and *to*; using *set* and *sit*; using *learn* and *teach*; using *right* and *write*; demonstrating comprehension by choosing the best word to complete a sentence; using creative ability to write a sentence; recognizing that a sentence begins with a capital letter and ends with the proper punctuation mark.

**Answer** the questions with complete sentences.  Answers vary.

1. What is our national bird?
   _____

   _____

2. What coin has the eagle on it?
   _____

   _____

3. Why do you think the eagle is our national bird?
   _____

   _____

**Circle** the correct word in parentheses.

1. Jeremy would like to  (teach, (learn))  how to play baseball.

2. Marcus  (may, (can))  carry heavy wood for the fireplace.

3. Did you  ((write), right)  a letter to our class missionary?

4. Mr. Jensen bought a  (blew, (blue))  truck.

5. Marie  ((set), sat)  her books by the door before she went to bed.

*Language Skills:* Demonstrating comprehension by answering questions; recognizing that a telling sentence begins with a capital letter and ends with a period; using *teach* and *learn, may* and *can, write* and *right, blew* and *blue, set* and *sat;* demonstrating comprehension by choosing the correct word                to complete a sentence.

Lesson 114    *Language 2*                                   114

**Write** yes in the blank if the
sentence is correct.
**Write** no if it is not correct.

yes    1. Mount Rushmore is a
monument to four men.

no    2. Did you know that Mount Rushmore is in
South Dakota.

no    3. men had to cut and carve the heads out of rock!

yes    4. All four of the men carved at Mount Rushmore
were Presidents.

no    5. Washington, Jefferson, Roosevelt, and Lincoln.

yes    6. Do you like Mount Rushmore?

**Arrange** these words in ABC order.

| Rushmore | monument | Lincoln |
|---|---|---|
| Washington | President | Jefferson |

1. Jefferson      4. President

2. Lincoln      5. Rushmore

3. monument      6. Washington

*Language Skills:* Demonstrating comprehension by deciding if a group of words is a sentence; recognizing that a
sentence begins with a capital letter and ends with the proper punctuation mark; alphabetizing—preparation for
using the dictionary.

     *Language 2*    Lesson 115

# Uncle Sam

Uncle Sam is a tall man dressed in red, white, and blue. He is a symbol of America. He stands for hard work, honesty, and loyalty. All Americans should be proud that Uncle Sam is one of our symbols of liberty.

**Answer** the questions about Uncle Sam by writing the answers in the puzzle.

**Down:**
1. People who live in America are called _____.

2. Another word for freedom is _____.

**Across:**
2. To stand true to your country is to be _____.

3. One symbol of America is Uncle _____.

4. The tall man is dressed in red, white, and _____.

5. Our country is called the _____ States.

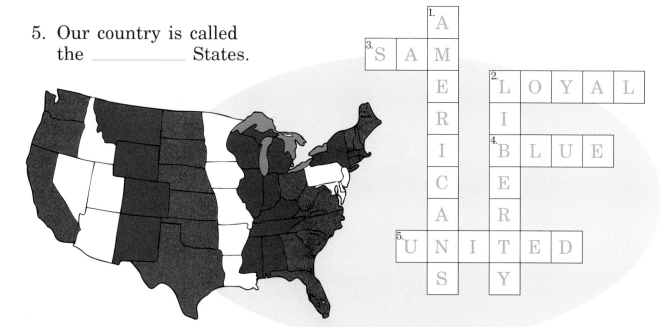

*Language Skills:* Reading with comprehension to learn facts; demonstrating comprehension by filling in the blanks correctly; solving a crossword puzzle.

**Write** contractions.

1. are not

   aren't

2. will not

   won't

3. you will

   you'll

4. is not

   isn't

5. they have

   they've

6. do not

   don't

7. could not

   couldn't

8. we will

   we'll

9. he will

   he'll

**Complete** the titles about America.

| **an American** | **Country** | **America** | **of Thee** |

1. God Bless America

2. This Is My Country

3. My Country 'Tis of Thee

4. I Am Thankful to Be an American

*Language Skills:* Forming contractions; demonstrating comprehension by choosing the correct word to complete a title; improving penmanship skills.

*Language 2*   Lesson 117

**Number** these words in ABC order.

<u>1</u> **c**at     <u>2</u> **d**og     <u>3</u> **d**uck     <u>4</u> **g**oat

1.   <u>4</u> **h**elmet

    <u>3</u> **g**love

    <u>2</u> **ba**t

    <u>1</u> **ba**ll

2.   <u>4</u> **p**ole

    <u>1</u> **b**ait

    <u>3</u> **h**ook

    <u>2</u> **f**ish

3.   <u>1</u> **f**ast

    <u>4</u> **w**ater

    <u>3</u> **s**pray

    <u>2</u> **f**ire

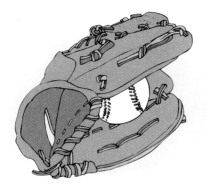  

**List** the symbols of America.

1.    eagle

2.    flag

3.    Uncle Sam

4.    Statue of Liberty

5.    Mount Rushmore

*Language Skills:* Alphabetizing—preparation for using the dictionary; compiling a list; spelling words in a list correctly.

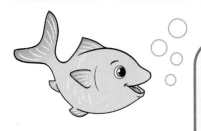

When a one-syllable root word ends with a short vowel and a consonant, double the consonant before adding a suffix beginning with a vowel.

flap    flaps    flapped    flapping

**Add** the suffix -ed or -ing to the root word.  Answers vary.

1. dig    digging

4. sob    sobbed

2. mop    mopped

5. tag    tagging

3. beg    begged

6. zip    zipping

**Write** nine words that remind you of the zoo.  Answers vary.

1. _____     4. _____     7. _____

2. _____     5. _____     8. _____

3. _____     6. _____     9. _____

**Write** one sentence using one of your zoo words.  Answers vary.

_____

_____

*Language Skills:* Forming words by adding the suffixes *ed* or *ing* to root words; spelling words correctly; using creative ability to write a sentence; recognizing that a sentence begins with a capital letter and ends with the proper punctuation mark.

**Write** a story about a visit to the zoo.

_____

Title
_____

_____

_____

_____

_____

_____

_____

_____

_____

_____

_____

_____

_____

_____

| | | | |
|---|---|---|---|
| wildest | funniest | gazelle | gorilla |
| biggest | ostrich | llama | alligator |
| smallest | deer | | elephants |

parrots
goats

_Language Skills:_ Using creative ability to write a story; recognizing that a sentence begins with a capital letter and ends with the appropriate punctuation; improving penmanship skills.

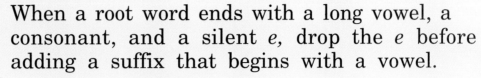

When a root word ends with a long vowel, a consonant, and a silent *e*, drop the *e* before adding a suffix that begins with a vowel.

bake
bakes
baked
baking

**Add** the suffix -ed or -ing to the root word.  Answers vary.

### shake — shaking

1. strike

   striking

2. race

   raced

3. arise

   arising

4. smile

   smiled

5. wire

   wired

6. cure

   curing

**Write** three sentences about going out to play in the snow, sliding down a hill, and throwing snowballs.

Answers vary.

*Language Skills:* Forming words by adding the suffix *ed* or *ing* to root words; using creative ability to write sentences; recognizing that a sentence begins with a capital letter and ends with the proper punctuation mark.

> Capitalize the names of holidays and special days.
>
> **Easter**
>
> **Veteran's Day**

Concept introduced in Phonics / Language 2 Curriculum, lesson 105.

**Rewrite** the holidays with the correct capitalization.

1. lincoln's birthday    Lincoln's Birthday

2. labor day    Labor Day

3. thanksgiving day    Thanksgiving Day

4. christmas    Christmas

5. flag day    Flag Day

**Match** the beginning of the sentence with the end of the sentence.

1. Most starfish have five      tiny eggs.

2. Baby starfish hatch from      suction tips on them.

3. His eyes cannot      arms.

4. Starfishes' arms have many      see things.

*Language Skills:* Capitalizing the names of holidays and special days; demonstrating comprehension by matching the end of a sentence with the beginning; reading to learn facts.

## Remember!

Capitalize the names of holidays and special days.

Christmas
Flag Day

**Circle** the letters that need to be capitalized.

1. v̇alentine's ḋay, l̇incoln's ḃirthday, and ẇashington's ḃirthday are in ḟebruary.

2. ėaster can be in ṁarch or ȧpril.

3. ṁemorial ḋay is in ṁay.

4. ȯn ḟlag ḋay and ịndependence ḋay we honor our country.

5. l̇abor ḋay and v̇eteran's ḋay are in the fall of the year.

6. ṫhanksgiving is always the fourth ṫhursday of ṅovember.

7. ịn ḋecember we have ċhristmas to honor the birth of Jesus.

**Write** one sentence about: Answers vary.

1. Valentine's Day _____

_____

_____

2. Christmas _____

_____

**Language Skills:** Capitalizing the names of holidays, special days, months, and days of the week and the first word in the sentence; reading with comprehension to learn facts; using creative ability to write sentences; recognizing that a sentence begins with a capital letter and ends with the proper punctuation mark.

 *Language 2* Lesson 123

**Add** the suffix -ed or -ing to the root word.   Answers vary.

1. save _____ saved _____  4. rope _____ roped _____

2. poke _____ poking _____  5. time _____ timing _____

3. ride _____ riding _____  6. quote _____ quoted _____

**Think** of this.   On a cold day after school you would like some hot chocolate.   How would you make it?   **Tell** how in five or six sentences.

_____ Answers vary. _____

_____

_____

_____

_____

_____

_____

_____

_____

_____

*Language Skills:* Forming words by adding the suffix *ed* or *ing* to root words; using creative ability to write instructions; recognizing that a telling sentence begins with a capital letter and ends with a period.

Lesson 124    *Language 2*
124

When a root word ends with a consonant and *y*, change the *y* to *i* before adding the suffix beginning with an *e*.

cry

cries        cried

crying       crier

**Add** the suffix -ed, -er, -en, -es, or -est to the root word.  Answers vary.

1. cozy      coziest         4. baby      babied

2. tiny      tinier         5. puppy      puppies

3. happy      happier         6. try      tries

**Write** three sentences about birds in the wintertime.  Birds need food during the winter snows.  How do they find their food?  Can you help them in any way?

Answers vary.

**Language Skills:** Forming words by adding the suffix *ed, er, en, es,* or *est* to root words (help students choose the correct suffix); using creative ability to write sentences; recognizing that a sentence begins with a capital letter and ends with a period.

       *Language 2*    Lesson 125

**Add** suffix -ed, -er, -es, or -est to the root word.  Answers vary.

1. pretty _____prettier_____      4. sleepy _____sleepiest_____

2. tidy _____tidied_____      5. dirty _____dirtier_____

3. carry _____carries_____      6. fuzzy _____fuzziest_____

**Write** two words to answer each question.  Answers vary.

1. What sounds would you hear during a snowstorm?

_____      _____

_____

2. What would you hear if you
   visited a hill with boys and
   girls sledding?

_____

_____

_____

3. What would you hear if a horse and sleigh went by your
   house?

_____      _____

_____      _____

4. What sounds would you hear at an ice skating rink?

_____      _____

_____      _____

*Language Skills:* Forming words by adding the suffix *ed, er, es,* or *est* to root words; demonstrating comprehension by answering questions.

**Read** the story.

# Rahab Is Saved

Joshua was the new leader of the children of Israel. He led them as they went into the land that God promised to them and took over the towns and cities. One day Joshua sent two spies to Jericho. When the soldiers came looking for them, Rahab hid the spies in her house. The spies promised Rahab that she and her family would be saved when Jericho was destroyed. She just had to hang a scarlet cord from her window. And that's exactly what happened. Jericho's walls fell down, but Rahab and her family were saved.

**Read** each sentence. **Number** them in order to show which things happened first.

3   Rahab hid the spies.

1   Joshua became leader.

5   Rahab and her family were saved.

2   Two spies went to Jericho.

4   Jericho's walls fell down.

**Circle** the letters that should be capitalized.
**Write** the correct punctuation at the end of each sentence.

1. On (f)riday we rode our bikes after school.

2. (d)id you know that (e)aster was in (a)pril this year?

3. (j)anuary and (f)ebruary are the coldest months.

4. (o)uch, you are on my foot!

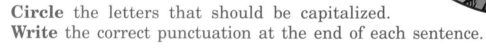

*Language Skills:* Reading with comprehension to learn facts; recognizing sequential order; capitalizing the names of the days and the months and the first word in a sentence; ending a sentence with the correct punctuation mark.

Read the story.

# Baby Seals

Baby seals are born with black fur and blue eyes. The mother seal takes care of her baby for a week and then leaves him for a while. The mother seal only checks on her baby from time to time. The baby plays with other young seals. He also learns to swim and catch fish for himself.

**Answer** the questions with complete sentences. Answers vary.

1. What do baby seals look like?

_____

_____

_____

_____

2. Who takes care of the baby seal?

_____

_____

_____

_____

3. What do baby seals do?

_____

_____

_____

_____

*Language Skills:* Reading with comprehension to learn facts; demonstrating comprehension by answering the questions correctly; recognizing that a telling sentence begins with a capital letter and ends with a period.

**Rewrite** each sentence in order.  **Put** in proper punctuation.

1. Gideon chose to lead God the army of Israel

   _God chose Gideon to lead the army of Israel._

2. men Three hundred picked by God were

   _Three hundred men were picked by God._

3. win helped them the battle God

   _God helped them win the battle._

Word Challenge

Can you **circle** the word that means almost the same as the word in the box?  Optional

| 1. tale | 2. ill | 3. close | 4. autumn |
|---------|--------|----------|-----------|
| read | bed | door | spring |
| (story) | well | (shut) | winter |
| book | (sick) | window | (fall) |

*Language Skills:* Demonstrating comprehension by arranging words correctly to form a sentence; recognizing that a telling sentence begins with a capital letter and ends with a period; reading to learn facts; identifying words with similar meanings.

**Write** a story about how Gideon defeated the Midianites.

Title _____

courage    knees

fearful    trumpet

afraid    pitchers

drink    lamps

lap    God's strength

*Language Skills:* Using creative ability to write a story; recognizing that a sentence begins with a capital letter and ends with the proper punctuation; improving penmanship skills.

Boots

Spotty

Puff

Tiger

Mittens

Kitty

Patches

Smoky

**Help** the cats find their dishes.
**Write** the cats' names on the dishes in ABC order.

1. Boots

3. Mittens

5. Puff

7. Spotty

2. Kitty

4. Patches

6. Smoky

8. Tiger

**Write** three sentences about a cat you enjoy playing with.
**Tell** what color the cat is and what it can do.

Answers vary.

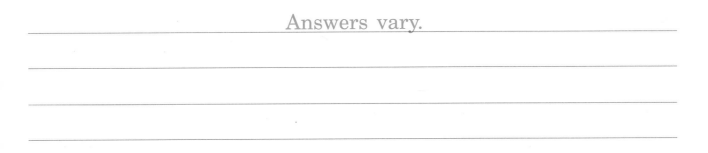

*Language Skills:* Alphabetizing—preparation for using the dictionary; using creative ability to write sentences; recognizing that a sentence begins with a capital letter and ends with the proper punctuation mark.

**Circle** each group of words that is a complete sentence.

1. (Alligators live near rivers and swamps.)

Alligators near swamps and marshes.

2. Alligators in the sun on river.

(They feel safer in the water.)

3. (He can open his eyes under water!)

His hide waterproof.

4. (Do you know how many teeth an alligator has?)

Eat fish, shrimp, turtles, and ducks.

5. (Mother alligators lay 20 to 60 eggs.)

She helps food.

6. (Large alligators are dangerous!)

Sound like fog horns.

**Write** a rhyming word.   Answers vary.

1. shell _____ bell

2. flop _____ chop

3. sound _____ round

4. treat _____ meat

5. right _____ light

6. dish _____ wish

**Language Skills:** Demonstrating comprehension by choosing the group of words that is a sentence; reading to learn facts; analyzing words to form rhyming words.

Lesson 132   *Language 2*                                    132

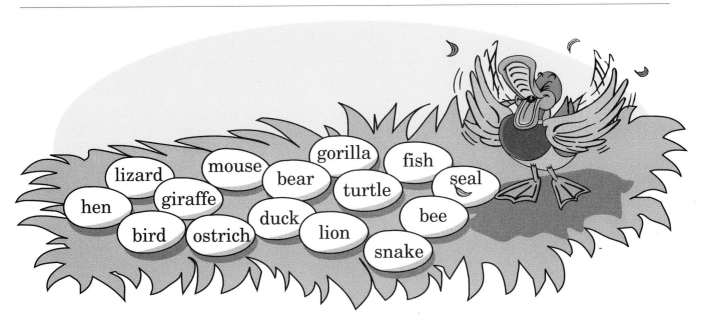

**Arrange** the words on the eggs in ABC order.

1. _____bear_____     6. _____giraffe_____     11. _____mouse_____

2. _____bee_____      7. _____gorilla_____     12. _____ostrich_____

3. _____bird_____     8. _____hen_____         13. _____seal_____

4. _____duck_____     9. _____lion_____        14. _____snake_____

5. _____fish_____     10. _____lizard_____     15. _____turtle_____

**Write** one sentence about the duck in the picture.

Answers vary.

_____

**Language Skills:** Alphabetizing—preparation for using the dictionary; using creative ability to write a sentence; recognizing that a sentence begins with a capital letter and ends with the proper punctuation mark.

**Add** 's to each word. Then **add** a word, telling something that belongs to each animal. Answers vary.

1. turtle **'s    eggs**

5. cat 's _____

2. seal 's _____

6. dog 's _____

3. crab 's _____

7. bird 's _____

4. duck 's _____

8. bear 's _____

**Answer** the questions in complete sentences. Answers vary.

1. Who is God the Son?

_____

_____

_____

2. Where is God the Son?

_____

_____

_____

3. Why did God the Son come to the earth?

_____

_____

_____

*Language Skills:* Using an apostrophe and an *s* to indicate ownership; demonstrating comprehension by answering questions correctly; recognizing that a telling sentence begins with a capital letter and ends with a period.

**Write** a story about Jesus as a boy.
**Tell** what you think he did each day
and how he might have helped Joseph.

Mary

Joseph

Jesus

carpenter

Title _____

Answers vary.

**Language Skills:** Using creative ability to write a story and a title; recognizing that a sentence begins with
a capital letter and ends with the proper punctuation mark.

© 1996 Pensacola Christian College • Not to be reproduced.          135          *Language 2*    Lesson 135

**Read** the story.

## Beavers

Beavers are large, brown, furry animals. They build their houses in the water. They have four teeth to cut down trees for their houses and for their food. Beavers have webbed back feet to help them in swimming.

Baby beavers grow up quickly. God made beavers so that they know how to swim without taking swimming lessons. They learn to obey their mother and father very quickly. If the babies hear the sound of a beaver tail being slapped in the water, they swim to a safe spot right away.

**Mark** the ○ beside the best answer.

1. Where do beavers live?

   ○ in the forest
   ◉ in the water
   ○ underground

2. Who teaches beavers how to swim?

   ○ their parents
   ○ their friends
   ◉ God

3. What do beavers eat?

   ○ flowers
   ○ grass
   ◉ wood

4. Why are beavers good swimmers?

   ◉ They have webbed feet.
   ○ They have thick fur.
   ○ They have sharp teeth.

*Language Skills:* Reading with comprehension to learn facts; demonstrating comprehension by answering questions correctly.

**Write** the sentences from Psalm 24 correctly on the lines below.
**Add** the correct punctuation.

1. Lord's is earth the The

   The earth is the Lord's.

2. ascend hill of shall Who into the Lord the

   Who shall ascend into the hill of the Lord?

3. glory this is of Who King

   Who is this King of glory?

**Circle** the two words in each row that are opposite.

| 1. (cold) (hot) day | 7. big (soft) (loud) |
| 2. (soft) dry (hard) | 8. (spend) thin (save) |
| 3. nice (dark) (light) | 9. (wise) give (fool) |
| 4. (quiet) big (noisy) | 10. (go) no (stop) |
| 5. (sweet) (sour) good | 11. (happy) long (sad) |
| 6. (old) small (new) | 12. (first) middle (last) |

*Language Skills:* Demonstrating comprehension by arranging words correctly to form sentences; identifying words having opposite meanings; ending a sentence with the proper punctuation.

*Language 2*   Lesson 137

An abbreviation is a shorter form of a longer word.
An abbreviation usually ends with a period.

Sunday — Sun.
January — Jan.

Concept introduced in Phonics/Language 2 Curriculum, lesson 136.

**Match** the day with its abbreviation.

1. Sunday        Sat.

2. Monday        Thurs.

3. Tuesday       Fri.

4. Wednesday     Sun.

5. Thursday      Mon.

6. Friday        Tues.

7. Saturday      Wed.

**Write** the abbreviation for each word.

Wednesday _____Wed._____        Tuesday _____Tues._____

Saturday _____Sat._____         Friday _____Fri._____

Sunday _____Sun._____           Monday _____Mon._____

**Answer** the question in a complete sentence.

# Where is the Lamb's Book of Life?

_____ It is in Heaven. _____

*Language Skills:* Abbreviating the days of the week; using creative ability to answer a question; recognizing that a sentence always begins with a capital letter and ends with proper punctuation.

## Remember!

An abbreviation is a shorter form of a longer word. It usually has a period.

Wednesday — Wed.
April — Apr.

**Match** the month with its abbreviation.
Some months do not have abbreviations.

1. January        May
2. February       June
3. March          Feb.
4. April          Jan.
5. May            Mar.
6. June           Apr.

7. July           Sept.
8. August         Nov.
9. September      July
10. October       Dec.
11. November      Aug.
12. December      Oct.

**Write** the abbreviation for each month.

1. December _____ Dec.

2. February _____ Feb.

3. August _____ Aug.

4. September _____ Sept.

5. November _____ Nov.

*Language Skills:* Abbreviating the months of the year; improving penmanship skills.

139 *Language 2* Lesson 139

**Read** the beginning sentence.
**Finish** the story.
**Write** a title for the story.

Title _____

One day I saw an octopus in the shoe store.

Answers vary.

*Language Skills:* Reading with comprehension to learn facts; using creative ability to write a story and a title; recognizing that a sentence begins with a capital letter and ends with the proper punctuation mark.

Lesson 140    *Language 2*

140

There are two sentences on each line.
**Write** each one correctly.

1. crabs have eight legs crabs have two claws

   a. _____ Crabs have eight legs. _____

   b. _____ Crabs have two claws. _____

2. crabs live near water most crabs have shells

   a. _____ Crabs live near water. _____

   b. _____ Most crabs have shells. _____

3. crabs can move quickly it is hard to catch crabs

   a. _____ Crabs can move quickly. _____

   b. _____ It is hard to catch crabs. _____

4. what do crabs eat they eat other sea animals

   a. _____ What do crabs eat? _____

   b. _____ They eat other sea animals. _____

*Language Skills:* Recognizing that a sentence begins with a capital letter and ends with the proper punctuation mark; reading with comprehension to learn facts; improving penmanship skills.

At the beach one day you decide to catch a crab for a pet.
In six sentences, tell how you would do it.
Tell these things:  (1) how to find a crab, (2) how to catch a crab,
(3) how to keep a crab, (4) what you would name a crab.

**Look** carefully to find what is missing in each picture.
**Write** a sentence to tell about it.  Answers vary.

1.

2.

*Language Skills:* Using creative ability to write sentences; recognizing that a sentence begins with a capital letter and ends with the proper punctuation mark; analyzing a picture to find the mistake.

**Complete** each sentence. Answers vary.

1. A jellyfish is like jelly because

_____

_____

2. A tadpole is like a fish except

_____

_____

3. A sea horse is like a horse because

_____

_____

4. A starfish is like a star except

_____

_____

5. A sand dollar is like a silver dollar because

_____

_____

6. Seaweed is like a weed because

_____

_____

*Language Skills:* Demonstrating comprehension and creative ability by correctly completing a sentence; ending a telling sentence with a period; improving penmanship skills.

**Read** the story.

## Samson

Samson had been tricked!  Delilah told the enemy Philistines that Samson's hair was the key to his great strength.  Quickly they shaved off his hair and captured him.  He had no power to get away.  The Philistines made fun of Samson and even put out his eyes, but slowly his hair began to grow back and his strength returned.  At a Philistine feast one day, Samson asked a boy to lead him to the middle pillars of the temple.  Samson prayed for strength and then began to push the pillars.  The temple crashed in a big heap.  The enemies were killed and Samson was, too.

**Read** the sentences.  **Number** them in order to show which things happened first.

  3    The Philistines put out Samson's eyes.

  5    Samson killed the enemy.

  4    The Philistines had a feast.

  2    Samson's hair was cut off.

  1    Delilah told the secret of Samson's strength.

**Write** a sentence about what is missing from each picture.

1.                        Answers vary.

2.

*Language Skills:* Reading with comprehension to learn facts; recognizing sequential order; analyzing a picture to find the mistakes; using creative ability to write sentences; recognizing that a sentence begins with a capital letter and ends with the proper punctuation mark.

Lesson 144    *Language 2*                144

**Write** a story about the
last few days of Jesus' life.
The words might help you.

Calvary       tomb
Jerusalem     soldier
disciples     grave
high priest

Title

Answers vary.

*Language Skills:* Using creative ability to write about Jesus; recognizing that a sentence begins with a capital letter and ends with the proper punctuation mark; improving penmanship skills.

**List** 7 things you see in the classroom.  **Write** a sentence for each one.

| chalk | My teacher uses **chalk** to write on the chalkboard. |

1.  Answers vary.

2.

3.

4.

5.

6.

7.

*Language Skills:* Using creative ability to write sentences; recognizing that a sentence begins with a capital letter and ends with the proper punctuation mark; improving penmanship skills.

**Copy** these sentences, making contractions out of the underlined words.

1. <u>I am</u> going to the grocery store.

   **I'm going to the grocery store.**

2. <u>She will</u> be able to take the trip.

   She'll be able to take the trip.

3. <u>Have not</u> we had enough work?

   Haven't we had enough work?

**Read** the story.
**Finish** it in your own words.

## My Sandwich

   One Saturday, I decided to make a sandwich. My sandwich would be the biggest and the best sandwich that had ever been made. I started making it in the morning so it would be done by lunch time. I planned to begin with a large loaf of bread. Then I opened the cupboard and refrigerator to find all the ingredients I would need. I piled on

Answers vary.

*Language Skills:* Reading a story with comprehension and using creative ability to complete it; recognizing that a sentence begins with a capital letter and ends with the proper punctuation mark.

**List** 7 things you could find at your house.
**Write** a sentence about each one.

1.  _Answers vary._

2.  _____

3.  _____

4.  _____

5.  _____

6.  _____

7.  _____

*Language Skills:* Using creative ability to write sentences; recognizing that a sentence begins with a capital letter and ends with the proper punctuation mark; improving penmanship skills.

Lesson 148    *Language 2*

148

**Add** 's to the name.   **Write** something that could belong to that person.
Answers vary.

Joe's shoe

1. Dad 's _____

2. Mom 's _____

3. Pat 's _____

4. Tim 's _____

**Choose** a word to complete each sentence.
**Write** the answer in the puzzle.

fur     toads     mother     swim     turtles

1. Seals learn to _____swim_____ in the water
   very early.

2. _____Mother_____ seals take care of their babies
   for a short time.

3. _____Turtles_____ crawl on the
   land and swim in the water.

4. Frogs and _____toads_____
   hop and swim.

5. Baby seals are born with black _____fur_____ .

*Language Skills:* Using an apostrophe and an *s* to indicate ownership; demonstrating comprehension by
choosing the correct word to complete a sentence; solving a crossword puzzle; reading to learn facts.

149     *Language 2*    Lesson 149

**Read** the title.
**Write** a story about the title.

## If All the Clocks Stopped Working

Answers vary.

*Language Skills:* Using creative ability to write a story; recognizing that a sentence begins with a capital letter and ends with the proper punctuation mark; improving penmanship skills.

**Change** the y to i; **add** a suffix.

| -ed | -er | -en | -es | -est |

1. stony     stonier
2. dirty     dirtiest
3. fuzzy     fuzziest

4. kindly     kindliest
5. lively     livelier
6. happy     happiest

**Traveling West**

**breakfast**
**campfire**
**scout**
**wagon master**
**Indians**
**circle**

**Put** yourself into this picture. **Tell** about some of the things you would do in the morning, daytime, and the evening while on the trail. The words might help you.

Answers vary.

**Language Skills:** Forming words by adding the suffix *ed, es, en, es,* or *est* to root words; using creative ability to write a story; recognizing that a sentence begins with a capital letter and ends with the proper punctuation mark; improving penmanship skills.

    *Language 2*   Lesson 151

**Finish** the sentences.

| exclamation | question | capital | sentence |

1. All sentences begin with a _____capital_____ letter.

2. A _____sentence_____ is a group of words that expresses a complete thought

3. A sentence that asks something is a _____question_____ .

4. A sentence that shows excitement ends with an _____exclamation_____ point.

**Circle** the letters that need to be capitals.
**Circle** the correct punctuation for the sentence.

1. coral is the skeleton of a tiny animal  ?  .  !

2. a piece of coral is really thousands of tiny animals  ?  .  !

3. do you know where coral lives  ?  .  !

4. living coral has many colors, but dead coral is white  ?  .  !

5. what a beautiful pink coral  ?  .  !

6. watch out; coral is sharp  ?  .  !

*Language Skills:* Demonstrating comprehension by choosing the correct word to complete a sentence; recognizing that a sentence begins with a capital letter and ends with the proper punctuation mark.

**Answer** the questions
in complete sentences.
Answers vary.

1. What things would you wear if you were a fisherman?

2. What kinds of things would you take on a fishing trip?

3. What kind of fish would you catch?

4. Where would you go fishing?

**Write** two questions you have about fish.

**How** do they breathe?

**When**

**Where**

*Language Skills:* Demonstrating comprehension by answering questions correctly; using creative ability to write questions; recognizing that a telling sentence begins with a capital letter and ends with a period.

**Make** each group of words into a
sentence by adding one of the words below.
**Write** the sentence on the line.

**head    evil    my    leadeth**

1. The Lord is shepherd.

   _The Lord is my shepherd._

2. He me beside the still water.

   _He leadeth me beside the still water._

3. I will fear no.

   _I will fear no evil._

4. Thou anointest my with oil.

   _Thou anointest my head with oil._

**Divide** these words between a vowel and a consonant.

1. b e | l o w          5. t i | n y

2. m a | p l e          6. B i | b l e

3. l a | d y            7. p i | l o t

4. p u | p i l          8. s i | l e n t

*Language Skills:* Demonstrating comprehension by choosing the correct word to complete a sentence; reading to learn about God; syllabicating.

**Write** six sounds you would
hear by a pond.  Answers vary.

**Write** four sentences about things that happen at a pond.  Answers vary.

1. _____

2. _____

3. _____

4. _____

**Write** a good title for a story about the picture.  Answers vary.

_____

*Language Skills:* Using creative ability to write a title and sentences; spelling words correctly; recognizing
that a sentence begins with a capital letter and ends with the proper punctuation mark.

   *Language 2*  Lesson 155

**Write** a story about one of the animals above.  **Tell** what the animal looks like, what he eats, where he lives, and who his enemies are.

_____

- - - - - - - - - - - - - - - - - - - - - - - - - - - -

- - - - - - - - - - - - - - - - - - - - - - - - - - - -

- - - - - - - - - - - - - - - - - - - - - - - - - - - -

- - - - - - - - - - - - - - - - - - - - - - - - - - - -

- - - - - - - - - - - - - - - - - - - - - - - - - - - -

- - - - - - - - - - - - - - - - - - - - - - - - - - - -

**Write** the abbreviation for each of these words.

| | | |
|---|---|---|
| 1. February | Feb. | |
| 2. Monday | Mon. | |
| 3. Thursday | Thurs. | |
| 4. August | Aug. | |
| 5. October | Oct. | |
| 6. Saturday | Sat. | |

**Write** two sentences about your favorite month of the year.
**Tell** why it is your favorite month and what you do during that month.

- - - - - - - - - - - - - - - - - - - - - - - - - - - -

- - - - - - - - - - - - - - - - - - - - - - - - - - - -

- - - - - - - - - - - - - - - - - - - - - - - - - - - -

_Language Skills:_ Using creative ability to write a title and a story; recognizing that a sentence begins with a capital letter and ends with the proper punctuation mark.  (If available, let the students read a simple article describing one of the animals before writing their reports, or read an article to the students.)  Abbreviating the months of the year and days of the week; using creati ability to write sentences.  **156**

Lesson 156    _Language 2_

## Abbreviations to Know

| | | |
|---|---|---|
| inch — in. | yard — yd. | pint — pt. |
| foot — ft. | mile — mi. | quart — qt. |

| | | | |
|---|---|---|---|
| gallon — gal. | minute — min. | month — mo. | ounce — oz. |
| second — sec. | hour — hr. | year — yr. | pound — lb. |

**Match** each word with its abbreviation.

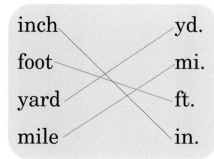

| | |
|---|---|
| inch | yd. |
| foot | mi. |
| yard | ft. |
| mile | in. |

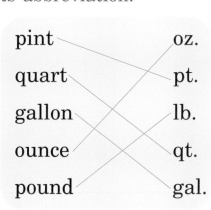

| | |
|---|---|
| pint | oz. |
| quart | pt. |
| gallon | lb. |
| ounce | qt. |
| pound | gal. |

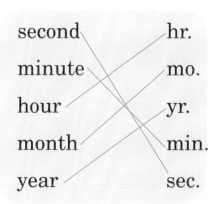

| | |
|---|---|
| second | hr. |
| minute | mo. |
| hour | yr. |
| month | min. |
| year | sec. |

**Fill in** the blanks using the abbreviations from above.

1. 60 sec. = 1 ___min.___
2. 12 ___mo.___ = 1 yr.
3. 16 oz. = 1 ___lb.___
4. 4 ___qt.___ = 1 gal.

5. 1 hr. = 60 ___min.___
6. 3 ft = 1 ___yd.___
7. 1 ft. = 12 ___in.___
8. 2 pt. = 1 ___qt.___

**Match** the word with its abbreviation.

| | |
|---|---|
| 1. Doctor | Mrs. |
| 2. Mister | Dr. |
| 3. Mistress | Mr. |

*Language Skills:* Abbreviating English measures; abbreviating personal titles.

*Language 2*   Lesson 157

**Number** each abbreviation with the same number as the word.

| | | | |
|---|---|---|---|
| 1. Doctor | ( 3 ) Tues. | 6. month | ( 8 ) Mar. |
| 2. January | ( 1 ) Dr. | 7. Mistress | ( 6 ) mo. |
| 3. Tuesday | ( 4 ) pt. | 8. March | ( 7 ) Mrs. |
| 4. pint | ( 5 ) Feb. | 9. foot | (10) Sat. |
| 5. February | ( 2 ) Jan. | 10. Saturday | ( 9 ) ft. |
| 11. second | (15) Nov. | 16. April | (19) Mr. |
| 12. September | (11) sec. | 17. Monday | (16) Apr. |
| 13. yard | (12) Sept. | 18. pound | (20) Wed. |
| 14. Thursday | (13) yd. | 19. Mister | (18) lb. |
| 15. November | (14) Thurs. | 20. Wednesday | (17) Mon. |
| 21. hour | (25) in. | 26. October | (27) Fri. |
| 22. quart | (23) Aug. | 27. Friday | (29) Dec. |
| 23. August | (22) qt. | 28. ounce | (30) Sun. |
| 24. year | (21) hr. | 29. December | (26) Oct. |
| 25. inch | (24) yr. | 30. Sunday | (28) oz. |

*Language Skills:* Abbreviating English measures, personal titles, days of the week, and months of the year.

Add the suffix -ed to these words.  Write the word.

## snap — snapped

1. clip      clipped      3. flop      flopped
2. skin      skinned      4. chat      chatted

## close — closed

1. shape      shaped      3. flame      flamed
2. snore      snored      4. trade      traded

## try — tried

1. cry      cried      3. spy      spied
2. marry      married      4. carry      carried

Think of a dog that does tricks.
Write three sentences about his tricks.

## Dog Tricks

Answers vary.

*Language Skills:* Forming words by adding the suffix *ed* to root words; using creative ability to write sentences; recognizing that a sentence begins with a capital and ends with the proper punctuation mark; improving penmanship skills.

*Language 2*    Lesson 159

**Write** a story about a camping trip. **Tell** where you went, how long you stayed, things you saw, and what you did. The words may help you.

Title _____

Answers vary.

sleeping bag   fishing   tent
camper   hiking   lake
campfire   camera
mountains   pictures

*Language Skills:* Using creative ability to write a story; recognizing that a sentence begins with a capital and usually ends with a period; improving penmanship skills.

**Write** nine words that remind you of spring.  *Answers vary.*

1. _____  4. _____  7. _____

2. _____  5. _____  8. _____

3. _____  6. _____  9. _____

**Use** some of your words to write four interesting sentences about spring.

*Answers vary.*

_____

_____

_____

_____

**Pretend** you are in the park in the springtime.
**Write** about what you would see and hear.

_____

Title

_____

_____

_____

_____

_____

_____

_____

*Language Skills:* Using creative ability to write sentences; spelling words correctly; recognizing that a
sentence begins with a capital letter and ends with the proper punctuation mark.

**Think** of the wind blowing over a hill. **Pretend** you are a kite. **Write** about what you would do, where you would fly, and what you would see.

### If I Were a Kite

_____
_____
_____
_____
_____
_____

**Name** six of the most beautiful things you have ever seen.

1. _____     4. _____

2. _____     5. _____

3. _____     6. _____

**Describe** three of the things you have named above.

1. _____

2. _____

3. _____

_Language Skills:_ Using creative ability to write a story and sentences; spelling words correctly; recognizing that a sentence begins with a capital letter and ends with the proper punctuation mark.

Lesson 162    _Language 2_                162

**Study** the picture of the boys. **Describe** what the first boy was doing and why he looks so happy. **Describe** the second boy. Give your story a title.

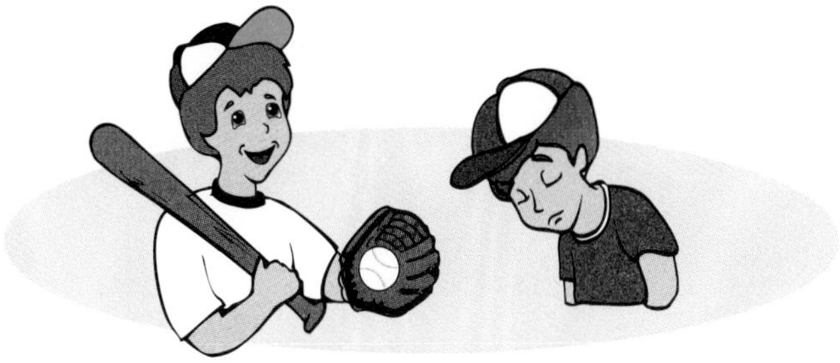

Title

**Write** a sentence using each of these words.

blessed

Answers vary.

thankful

praise

wonderful

**Read** the title and the beginning of the story.
**Finish** the story the way you believe it ended.

# My Favorite Friend

My friend is huge, fat, and furry. He loves to play games with me. I have shown him how to carry heavy loads, pick up things in the yard, and go for help if I'm having trouble.

One day, I was playing up in my tree house when the ladder fell down. My friend was on the ground and could not get the ladder back up.

_____

_____

_____

_____

_____

_____

_____

_____

_____

_____

*Language Skills:* Reading a story with comprehension; using creative ability to complete a story; recognizing that a sentence begins with a capital letter and ends with the proper punctuation mark.

**Write** five ways in which you can obey your parents.
**Give** examples of when and how to obey.
Answers vary.

## Ways I Can Obey My Parents

1. _____

_____

2. _____

_____

3. _____

_____

4. _____

_____

5. _____

_____

*Language Skills:* Using creative ability to write about obedience; recognizing that a sentence begins
with a capital letter and ends with the proper punctuation mark.

*Language 2* Lesson 165

**Write** one sentence telling what you would like to be when you grow up.

Answers vary.

**Write** three reasons why you want to be that?

Answers vary.

**Write** about two ways you can prepare for that job.

Answers vary.

*Language Skills:* Using creative ability to write about future plans and present preparation; recognizing that a sentence begins with a capital letter and ends with the proper punctuation mark.

Find the hidden sentences. **Write** them on the lines.
**Begin** sentences with capital letters, and **use** correct punctuation.

I can swim.

| I | N | S | M |
|---|---|---|---|
| C | A | W | I |

1.

| T | L | I | T | B |
|---|---|---|---|---|
| U | S | K | A | U |
| R | E | E | E | G |
| T | L | T | O | S |

1. _____

2. _____

2.

| G | R | E | T | O |
|---|---|---|---|---|
| O | A | G | S | H |
| L | H | O | T | A |
| D | S | O | E | V |
| F | I | D | P | E |

**Complete** each sentence on the lines below.  Answers vary.

1. Ten bluebirds _____

2. The mother duck _____

3. An American eagle _____

**Language Skills:** Solving puzzles; recognizing that a telling sentence begins with a capital letter and ends with a period; reading sentences with comprehension; using creative ability to complete sentences.

**Complete** each sentence on the lines below.  Answers vary.

1. My brother

2. A little gray mouse

3. The old lamp

4. Grandmother

5. The strong wind

6. Rainy days

7. The lonely dog

8. My mother

9. Our tree house

*Language Skills:* Demonstrating comprehension by correctly completing the sentences; using creative ability to complete sentences; recognizing that a telling sentence begins with a capital letter and ends with a period.

**List** some places you have visited, would like
to visit, or plan to visit this summer. Answers vary.

1. _____    4. _____

2. _____    5. _____

3. _____    6. _____


**Write** about one of the places you have listed above.
**Tell** what you can do there.

_____

_____

_____

_____

_____

_____

_____

_____

**Write** nine words that remind you of summer fun.   Answers vary.

1. _____      4. _____      7. _____

2. _____      5. _____      8. _____

3. _____      6. _____      9. _____

**Study** the picture.   **Write** sentences telling what is happening.

Answers vary.

*Language Skills:* Using creative ability to write sentences describing a picture; recognizing that a sentence begins with a capital letter and ends with the proper punctuation mark.

You may wish to have students recopy thank-you note from p. 80, address it, and mail it.

first fol

From: _____

_____

_____

_____

place
stamp
here

To: _____

_____

_____

_____

second fol

# Word Challenge:

## Expanding Language Skills through Reading

Second graders have words in their speaking vocabulary that they may not have seen in printed form. The following word lists have been compiled to provide an opportunity for students to read these commonly used words.

While reading these lists, students will be applying phonics sounds they have learned and increasing their reading speed. Encourage students to read quickly and accurately, but to speak clearly.

These word lists may also be used for reference during creative writing exercises throughout the year.

# FOODS

### A
**(meats/seafood)**
bacon
beef
chicken
clams
cold cuts
crab
fish
hamburger
hot dogs
lamb
oysters
pork chops
pork roast
sausage
scallops
shrimp
steak
veal

### B
**(fruits)**
apples
bananas
blackberries
cantaloupe
cherries
grapefruit
grapes
kiwi
lemons
limes
melons
oranges
peaches
pears
plums
strawberries
watermelon

### C
**(vegetables)**
beans
beets
broccoli
Brussels sprouts
cabbage
carrots
cauliflower
celery
cucumbers
lettuce
okra
onions
peas
peppers
potatoes
spinach
sweet corn
tomatoes
zucchini

### D
**(condiments)**
butter
garlic
horseradish
jam
jelly
ketchup
margarine
mayonnaise
mustard
pepper
relish
salad dressing
salsa
salt
seasoning salt
taco sauce

### E
**(dairy)**
butter
buttermilk
cheese
cottage cheese
ice cream
margarine
milk
sour cream
whipped cream
yogurt

### F
**(breads)**
bagels
biscuits
corn bread
crescent rolls
croissants
danishes
dinner rolls
muffins
scones
sourdough

### G
**(pasta)**
cannelloni
fettuccine
lasagna noodles
linguine
macaroni
manicotti
ravioli
spaghetti
vermicelli

### H
**(bakery items)**
cake
croissant
danish
donut
doughnut
muffin
pastry
pie
truffle

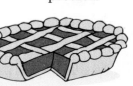

### I
**(snacks)**
candy
caramel corn
crackers
popcorn
potato chips
pretzels

### J
**(beverages)**
hot chocolate
iced tea
juice
lemonade
milk
milkshake
punch
soda
water

### K
**(grocery store)**

| | |
|---|---|
| canned goods | fresh produce |
| cash register | grocery store |
| cashier | manager |
| check | scanner |
| dairy case | shopping cart |
| deli | supermarket |

### L
**(restaurant)**

| | | |
|---|---|---|
| appetizer | hash browns | soup |
| baked potato | macaroni and | spaghetti |
| beverage | cheese | steak |
| booth | menu | stew |
| cash register | pizza | sub sandwich |
| chili | pork roast | table |
| French fries | restaurant | tacos |
| grilled fish | salad bar | tip |
| hamburgers | server | |

174

# OUTDOOR THINGS

**A**
**(weather)**

clouds
fog
hail
hurricane
ice
lightning
rain
rainbow
sleet
snow
sunshine
thunder
tornado
tropical storm
wind

**B**
**(activities)**

camping
collecting
cycling
fishing
football
hiking
horseback
  riding
ice skating
roller blading
running
skiing
sledding
soccer
swimming
tennis

**C**
**(outdoor jobs)**

barbecuing
  meat
mowing grass
painting fences
planting flowers
raking leaves
sweeping
  sidewalks
washing cars
washing
  windows
watering plants
weeding
  gardens

**D**
**(pond animals)**

beaver
duck
fish
frog
salamander
snake
swan
tadpole
turtle

**E**
**(forest animals)**

badger
bat
bear
chipmunk
deer
field mouse
fox
frog
mole
moose
mouse
opossum
otter
pheasant
rabbit
raccoon
rat
skunk
squirrel
turkey
weasel
woodpecker

**F**
**(insects)**

ant
aphid
beetle
bumblebee
butterfly
cicada
cricket
dragonfly
flea
gnat
grasshopper
hornet
housefly
katydid
ladybug
locust
mosquito
moth
roach
spider
stinkbug
walking stick
wasp
yellow jacket

**G**
**(flowers)**

buttercups
carnations
chrysanthemums
crocus
daffodils
daisies
dandelions
honeysuckle
hyacinth
lilacs
lilies
marigolds
orchids
pansies
petunias
phlox
poinsettia
roses
sunflowers
tulips
violets

**H**
**(trees)**

apple
aspen
beech
birch
cedar
cherry
chestnut
cypress
elm
fir
hickory
magnolia
maple
myrtle
oak
palm
pear
pecan
pine
redwood
sequoias
spruce
walnut
willow

# PLACES

| A (at school) | B (around town) | C (at the park) | D (on the farm) | E (construction site) |
|---|---|---|---|---|
| arithmetic | baker | ball | barn | backhoe |
| art | bank | balloon | bull | building |
| Bible | beautician | bench | calf | materials |
| books | bookstore | bicycle | chicks | bulldozer |
| building | bus station | birds | combine | caution |
| bulletin boards | butcher shop | boat | harvester | cement |
| chalkboard | cafe | boys | corn | concrete mixer |
| charts | church | children | cow | construction |
| classes | city hall | chipmunks | dairy barn | conveyor belts |
| classroom | courthouse | cotton candy | dog | cranes |
| desks | drugstore | dogs and cats | donkey | derrick |
| globe | fruit market | exercise | duck | drill |
| hallways | grocery store | flowers | farmer | dump trucks |
| health | hairdresser | girls | farmhouse | electrical wiring |
| history | hardware store | grass | field | foreman |
| jungle gym | hospital | ice cream | goat | front-end loader |
| maps | library | joggers | goose | hardhat |
| merry-go-round | mall | jump rope | hay | jackhammer |
| monkey bars | newsstand | jungle gym | hen | reduced speed |
| music | parking garage | kite | henhouse | scraper |
| paper | pet store | paths | horse | steel girders |
| pencil | plaza | people | lamb | tractor |
| playground | police station | pond | orchard | workmen |
| principal | post office | roller blades | pig | wrecking ball |
| reading | railway station | roller skates | pigsty | |
| science | restaurant | skateboards | plow | |
| seesaw | school | slide | rooster | |
| slide | service station | squirrels | scarecrow | |
| students | shoe store | stroller | shed | |
| study | shopping center | swing | sheep | |
| swings | sports arena | trees | stable | |
| teachers | supermarket | | tractor | |
| writing | toy store | | wagon | |
| | | | weather vane | |

| F | G | H | I | J |
|---|---|---|---|---|
| **(zoo)** | **(music store)** | **(at a party)** | **(circus)** | **(seashore)** |
| alligator | accordion | balloons | animals | beach |
| bear | cello | cake | band | crabs |
| crocodile | clarinet | candles | big top | jellyfish |
| elephant | cymbals | cards | cages | ocean |
| flamingo | drums | decorations | clowns | pail |
| giraffe | flute | drinks | cotton candy | sand |
| hippopotamus | French horn | friends | elephants | sand castle |
| jaguar | guitar | guests | fire-eaters | sand dollars |
| kangaroo | harmonica | ice cream | juggler | seaweed |
| leopard | harpsichord | icing | noise | shells |
| lion | keyboard | invitations | peanuts | shovel |
| monkey | organ | party favors | ringmaster | starfish |
| orangutan | piano | party hats | tickets | sunset |
| ostrich | saxophone | presents | tigers | surf |
| panda | triangle | streamers | tightrope | swimming |
| parrot | trombone | surprises | trailers | swimsuit |
| peacock | trumpet | | trapeze | wading |
| penguin | viola | | | water |
| sea lion | violin | | | waves |
| snake | xylophone | | | |
| tiger | | | | |
| toucan | | | | |
| zebra | | | | |

# HOME

### A
**(types of homes / places to stay)**

apartment
bed-and-
   breakfast inn
cabin
condominium
cottage
duplex
high-rise
hotel
mansion
motel
tent
town house

### B
**(kitchen)**

blender
breadbox
can opener
coffee maker
cupboard
dishwasher
frying pan
garbage
   disposal
ice maker
kettle
microwave oven
mixer
refrigerator
shelf
stove
teapot
toaster
toaster oven
trash compactor
waffle iron

### C
**(dining room)**

chairs
china
china cabinet
clock
crystal
cup
fork
hot plates
hutch
knife
napkins
napkin rings
pitcher
place mats
saucer
spoon
table
tablecloth

### D
**(laundry room / cleaning closet)**

broom
cleanser
detergent
dryer
dustpan
fabric softener
iron
ironing board
laundry basket
mop
rags
scrub brush
sponge
washing
   machine

### E
**(living room / family room)**

armchair
books
carpet
cassette tape
ceiling fan
compact discs
computer
couch
curtains
cushions
drapes
end tables
entertainment
   center
family Bible
magazines
piano
pillows
recliner
remote control
rocking chair
sofa
stereo system
television
video cassette
wallpaper

### F
**(bathroom)**

| | |
|---|---|
| bathtub | powder |
| bubble bath | shampoo |
| brush | shower |
| comb | shower curtain |
| conditioner | sink |
| dental floss | soap |
| drain | toothbrush |
| faucet | toothpaste |
| hair spray | towel |
| makeup | washcloth |
| mirror | |

### G
**(bedroom)**

| | |
|---|---|
| alarm clock | dresser |
| bathrobe | housecoat |
| bed | lamps |
| bedspread | mirror |
| blankets | nightgown |
| bureau | pajamas |
| cedar chest | pillows |
| closet | quilt |
| comforter | sheets |
| drapes | |

## H
### (closet / drawers)

bathrobe
belt
blouse
blue jeans
boots
clothing
dress
dress shirt
gloves
jacket
overalls
pajamas
pants

raincoat
scarf
shoes
skirt
slippers
socks
suit
sweater
sweat suit
swimsuit
tie
umbrella
vest

## I
### (yard)

asphalt
barbecue
birdhouse
carport
driveway
flowers
mailbox
pavement
porch
roof
sprinkler
swimming pool
swings
tree house
trees

## J
### (garage)

bicycle pump
broom
ladder
lawn mower
paintbrush
pitchfork
rake
shovel
spade
trash can
watering can
wheelbarrow

## K
### (tool shed)

electric drill
hammer
ladder
nails
pliers
sander
saw
screwdriver
toolbox
workbench
wrench

## L
### (study / office)

bookcase
calculator
calendar
desk
drawers
file cabinet
paper clips
pencil
pens
rubber bands
ruler

## M
### (people)

aunt
brother
cousin
father
grandfather
grandmother
mother
nephew
niece
sister
uncle

## N
### (toys)

balloon
bulldozer
crayons
drum
jack-in-the-box
jump rope
puzzle
roller blades
train
wagon
whistle

## O
### (pets)

cage
cat
dog
fish
gerbil
guinea pig
hamster
kitten
mouse
pet food
puppy
rabbit
turtle
veterinarian

## P
### (handwork / sewing)

buttons
cloth
counted
  cross-stitch
crochet
embroidery
macramé
needlepoint
pattern
quilting
scissors
sewing machine
thread
zipper

# TRAVEL / TRANSPORTATION

## A
### (ground travel)
causeway
caution
crosswalk
exit
fire hydrant
highway
interstate
pavement
pedestrian
speed bump
speed limit
stop sign
street lamp
traffic
traffic light
yield

## B
### (air travel)
airplane
airport
aviation
baggage
  carousel
business trip
first officer
flight attendant
glider
helicopter
hot air balloon
luggage
pilot
runway
security
terminal
twin engine
vacation

## C
### (water travel)
canoe
cargo ship
cruise
ferry
fishing boat
hovercraft
hydrofoil
kayak
leisure craft
lifeboat
life vest
motorboat
ocean liner
rowboat
sailboat
submarine
tanker
troller
tug
water skiing
wave runner
yacht

## D
### (space travel)
astronaut
capsule
control room
countdown
docking
launch pad
liftoff
lunar module
moon
orbit
rocket
satellite
space shuttle
space station
spacesuit

## E
### (vehicles)
ambulance
automobile
bicycle
bulldozer
bus
car
dump truck
eighteen
  wheeler
fire engine
freight train
garbage truck
golf cart
jeep
minivan
moped
motorcycle
motor home
passenger train
police car
school bus
tanker
train
truck

## F
### (car parts)
air filter
battery
brakes
defroster
door handles
engine
gas
gearshift
hood
keys
mirrors
oil
radio
steering wheel
tires
transmission
trunk
upholstery
vinyl
wheels
window handles
windows
windshield
  wipers

## G
### (repair and maintenance)
blowout
breakdown
dead battery
estimate
expensive
flat tire
garage
gas station
jumper cables
mechanic
oil change
repair
spark plugs
tire rotation
tow truck
tuneup
wrecker

## H
### (on the map)
avenue
boulevard
circle
city
continent
country
cul-de-sac
highway
interstate
ocean
parkway
province
river
road
sea
state
street
suburb
town
village

# MISCELLANEOUS

**A**
**(workers and helpers)**

architect
artist
attorney
author
bus driver
businessman
carpenter
dentist
doctor
editor
farmer
fireman
hairdresser
judge
lawyer
mail carrier
missionary
mother
nurse
pastor
policeman
salesperson
scientist
secretary
teacher
veterinarian

**B**
**(at the office)**

answering
    machine
board of
    directors
computer
copy machine
desks
elevator
fax machine
intercom
janitor
messages
microphone
pager
photocopy
president
printer
secretary
speaker phone
telephone
typewriter
vice president
windows

**C**
**(geography)**

bay
brook
canyon
cliff
creek
desert
geyser
gorge
gulf
gully
hills
island
meadow
mountain
ocean
peninsula
plains
river
sea
stream
valley
waterfall

**D**
**(parts of the body)**

ankle
arm
back
ear
elbow
eyes
feet
fingers
hair
hand
head
heel
hip
knee
leg
lips
mouth
neck
nose
shoulder
teeth
thumb
toes
tongue
wrist

**E**
**(emergency / medical)**

ambulance
doctor
examination
fireman
hospital
illness
intensive care
lights
medical
    technician
nurse
operation
paramedic
patient
pharmacy
policeman
prescription
sirens
surgery
X-ray

**F**
**(Christmas)**

angel
carols
donkey
eagerness
garland
gifts
Jesus
Joseph
lights
manger
Mary
mince pies

mistletoe
packages
presents
pudding
shepherds
stable
star
stockings
turkey
wise men
wreaths

**G**
**(mail)**

address
envelope
letter
letter carrier
mailbox
package
stamp
stationery
ZIP code

**(phone)**

advertisement
area code
assistance
busy signal
collect call
communication
directory
operator
Yellow Pages

**H**
**(information)**

almanac
atlas
book
computer
concordance
dictionary
encyclopedia
magazine
microfiche
newspaper
periodical
radio
television
video

# BOOKS OF THE BIBLE

## Old Testament

| | | | | |
|---|---|---|---|---|
| Genesis | 1 Samuel | Esther | Lamentations | Micah |
| Exodus | 2 Samuel | Job | Ezekiel | Nahum |
| Leviticus | 1 Kings | Psalms | Daniel | Habakkuk |
| Numbers | 2 Kings | Proverbs | Hosea | Zephaniah |
| Deuteronomy | 1 Chronicles | Ecclesiastes | Joel | Haggai |
| Joshua | 2 Chronicles | Song of Solomon | Amos | Zechariah |
| Judges | Ezra | Isaiah | Obadiah | Malachi |
| Ruth | Nehemiah | Jeremiah | Jonah | |

## New Testament

| | | | | |
|---|---|---|---|---|
| Matthew | 1 Corinthians | 1 Thessalonians | Hebrews | 2 John |
| Mark | 2 Corinthians | 2 Thessalonians | James | 3 John |
| Luke | Galatians | 1 Timothy | 1 Peter | Jude |
| John | Ephesians | 2 Timothy | 2 Peter | Revelation |
| Acts | Philippians | Titus | 1 John | |
| Romans | Colossians | Philemon | | |

# BIBLE NAMES

| A | | B | | C | | D |
|---|---|---|---|---|---|---|
| Adam | Rebekah | Moses | Goliath | Matthew | Lazarus | Simon Peter |
| Eve | Jacob | Joshua | Daniel | Mark | Nicodemus | Andrew |
| Cain | Rachel | Gideon | Shadrach | Luke | Paul | Philip |
| Abel | Joseph | Samson | Meshach | John | Silas | Thomas |
| Noah | Lot | Samuel | Abednego | Jesus | Timothy | James |
| Abraham | Jonah | Saul | | Mary | Zacchaeus | Thaddeus |
| Sarah | Esther | David | | Martha | | Simon |
| Isaac | | | | | | Judas |
| | | | | | | Bartholomew |

# CHURCH

| A (parts of the building) | B (people) | C (miscellaneous) |
|---|---|---|
| aisles | assistant pastor | Bible |
| auditorium | choir | choruses |
| choir loft | choir director | fellowship |
| fellowship hall | deacons | hymns |
| organ | minister of music | invitation |
| pews | organist | message |
| piano | pastor | offering |
| platform | pianist | orchestra |
| pulpit | secretary | prayer |
| sanctuary | Sunday school teacher | preaching |
| vestibule | ushers | verse memory |
| | youth director | visitation |

# SUFFIXES

**A**

| | | | | | |
|---|---|---|---|---|---|
| sit | sits | sitting | shop | shops | shopped |
| grin | grins | grinned | throb | throbs | throbbing |
| sled | sleds | sledding | drag | drags | dragged |

**B**

| | | | | | |
|---|---|---|---|---|---|
| stepped | tripping | plodding | stubbed | flopping | thudded |
| thinner | plugged | shutting | trapped | skinned | dropping |
| trapped | stopper | snipped | dripping | spinner | splitting |

**C**

| | | | | | |
|---|---|---|---|---|---|
| wipe | wipes | wipers | like | liked | likes |
| bounce | bounced | bouncy | shake | shakes | shaking |
| brake | braking | broken | cruise | cruising | cruiser |

**D**

| | | | | | |
|---|---|---|---|---|---|
| stroked | driving | greasy | sloping | thriving | clothing |
| freezer | stolen | traded | shiny | frozen | wasted |
| creases | smiled | shaky | flaming | stoked | scraped |

**E**

| | | | | | |
|---|---|---|---|---|---|
| happy | happier | happily | cozy | coziest | cozier |
| bouncy | bounciest | bouncier | wit | witty | wittiest |
| icy | icier | iciest | busy | busily | busiest |

**F**

| | | | | | |
|---|---|---|---|---|---|
| groceries | lazily | funnier | prettier | candies | shabbiest |
| hazier | puppies | breeziest | ladies | dustier | cities |
| dirtiest | healthier | babies | sleepily | mightiest | sandier |

**G**

| | | | | | |
|---|---|---|---|---|---|
| sandier | shaved | flipped | gloomily | shaping | shady |
| shining | shopping | draped | scratchiest | grimy | clippers |
| closer | reclining | grabbing | glimpses | friskiest | breathing |
| broken | creamiest | dreamily | primed | grating | shipped |

# CONTRACTIONS

**A**

| | | | |
|---|---|---|---|
| can—can't | could—couldn't | had—hadn't | did—didn't |
| shall—shan't | would—wouldn't | has—hasn't | does—doesn't |
| will—won't | should—shouldn't | have—haven't | do—don't |

**B**

| | | | | | |
|---|---|---|---|---|---|
| she'll | they'll | I'll | we'll | you'll | he'll |
| they've | you've | we've | I've | he's | she's |
| we'd | she'd | they'd | he'd | I'd | you'd |

_____ has caught on in Language!

_____ is a big-time story writer!

is a Punctuation Champ!

is a Super Story Writer!